1400
9933

Lectures in
Dynamic Psychiatry

LECTURES IN
DYNAMIC PSYCHIATRY

MILTON KURIAN, M.D., *editor*

MORTON H. HAND, M.D., *co-editor*

Brooklyn Psychiatric Society
New York

Distributed by
INTERNATIONAL UNIVERSITIES PRESS, INC., *New York*

Contents

Foreword

With the founding of the Brooklyn Psychiatric Society, in 1949, a forum for the exchange of psychiatric ideas in Brooklyn, N. Y., came to fruition. Its purpose was to maintain and encourage the growth of the highest scientific standards in the practice of psychiatry. The late Simon Rothenberg, M.D. (who introduced psychoanalysis to this locality) was its first president.

The society's members officially convened in four yearly academic sessions to hear and discuss the contributions of outstanding psychiatrists and psychoanalysts. But, this was insufficient. Certain members, intrigued by the dynamic impetus psychiatry has received from psychoanalysis, felt the need to meet more frequently for readings and seminar discussions. Plans to establish such a program were considered by succeeding presidents of the young but growing society, Sam Parker, M.D., and Joseph Abramson, M.D. The fourth president, Morton H. Hand, M.D., and his vice-president, David Engelhardt, M.D., who succeeded to the presidency, finally brought it into practice in 1958. Dr. Hand appointed a Committee on Postgraduate Education to be chaired by Dr. Engelhardt. However, since he was burdened with his duties as Acting Director of the Department of Psychiatry, State University of New York, Downstate Medical Center, George J. Train, M.D., was appointed acting chairman.

On February 3, 1958, the first meeting of this analytic program took place in the library of the Psychiatric Building of the Kings County Hospital. Meetings were held fortnightly thereafter and were devoted to psychoanalytic readings and continuous case seminars. These sessions continued until the summer of 1960, through the presidential term of Sidney Green, M.D. At this time a new format was held desirable and Dr. Green appointed Dr. Train to chair a committee to study possible solutions. Milton Kurian, M.D., was appointed its secretary and Drs. Morton Hand, Edward Kent, Abbott Lippman, and Adele Streeseman became its members. The committee obtained the assistance of Sandor Lorand, M.D., and a series of ten lectures was arranged. The aim of this series was to provide material which would be directly applicable to the treatment of the sick. The first lecture was presented by Dr. Lorand on October 5, 1960, in a lecture hall of the State University at Brooklyn, N. Y. If attendance is any criterion of both the needs of the group who gathered for these lectures and its adequate satisfaction, the course we have taken is a good beginning. Lectures were presented with an informal warmth which encouraged active audience participation and delightful side remarks. The proceedings were recorded on tape. Because these lectures are most timely and express current psychiatric thought, and, also, at the request of those psychiatrists who were unable to attend, the committee decided to publish them. This will enable us to share these experiences with colleagues who are equally desirous of keeping abreast with advances in analytic psychotherapy. This is the history of the lectures which follow.

Grateful acknowledgment is due Dr. Abbott Lippman, president of the Brooklyn Psychiatric Society during the year 1960-1961, for his support and active participation as a member of the committee; to Dr. Sandor Lorand for his inspiring and unstinting help; to Drs. Robert A. Moore (Dean, State University of New York, Downstate Medical Center), I. Charles Kaufman

(Professor and Chairman of the Department of Psychiatry), and Edward A. Falsey (Vice-President, Brooklyn Psychiatric Society) for arranging the use of the university halls. I wish finally to express tender gratitude to the members of the committee who labored diligently and long to bring our idea into practical application.

Plans for the future are hopeful. The Brooklyn Psychiatric Society is honored that cosponsorship in Postgraduate Psychiatry with the State University of New York, Downstate Medical Center, has been effected through Dr. Kaufman's efforts and his appointment of Dr. Sandor Lorand as Director of the Postgraduate Program in Psychiatry. The committee envisions this liaison as a virile and growing contribution to the professional enrichment of psychiatrists.

In the course of compiling these lectures, a great deal of labor was involved. Grateful recognition of the efforts of those who contributed in this area is acknowledged. The committee thanks Drs. Kurian and Hand, who shared the heroic task of editorship, the lecturers who reviewed and corrected their papers, Miss Hope N. Beliveau and Mrs. Jeanne O. Erles for their technical assistance, Dr. Abram Kagan, publisher, for his guidance and stimulating interest in preparing the material for the press. Finally, our thanks to the Merck, Sharp & Dohme Postgraduate Program, through whose kind assistance our program became a reality.

THE COMMITTEE ON POSTGRADUATE
EDUCATION FOR PSYCHIATRISTS:

George J. Train, M.D., Chairman
Milton Kurian, M.D., Secretary
Morton H. Hand, M.D.
Edward Kent, M.D.
Abbott Lippman, M.D.
Adele Streeseman, M.D.

Introduction

The essays in this volume originated as transcribed tape recordings of the actual lectures. The material was edited and submitted to the lecturers for correction, since the talks were originally given in a seminar-like manner.

The lecturers are all practicing psychoanalysts who are also interested in analytically oriented psychotherapy. They have all been engaged in the supervision of psychotherapy.

In organizing the lectures, controversial points about psychotherapeutic methods were avoided and emphasis was placed on the distinction between psychoanalysis proper and analytically oriented psychotherapy. The lecturers addressed an audience composed of practicing psychiatrists, (some of these physicians were then in analysis whereas others had already had personal analysis).

Freud's contribution to psychiatry was discussed in general. The role of the dynamic unconscious, the problems of regression, childhood sexuality, and the origins of mental conflicts received attention.

How mental conflicts originate was demonstrated with case material of the various types of neuroses. In this manner, the dynamics and structure of the origin of mental conflicts was made comprehensible. This knowledge makes it easier for the therapist to arrive at a proper diagnosis and to assess the prognosis of therapeutic processes.

The importance of regressive tendencies in neurosis and psychosis was demonstrated, especially with examples from dream material. The technique of stopping and undoing regressive tendencies was illustrated and discussed.

All the lectures are oriented toward technique. They make easy reading, avoid unnecessary theorizing, and use clinical demonstrations to substantiate theoretical conceptions.

This volume is for those who are interested in furthering their own therapeutic techniques and comparing the techniques of various authorities in psychiatry. It may stimulate new insight and new approaches. The reader will find that ego problems are in the center of the discussions, since it is recognized that psychotherapy has, as its aim, the liberation and redistribution of psychic energies, with allocation of more energy to the ego. The aim of strengthening the ego thus makes the ego the center of concern (theoretically and practically). Thus, the therapeutic process will always center around the ramifications of both the ego and id.

SANDOR LORAND, M.D.
New York, January 1963

Some Basic Concepts of the Dynamics of Therapy

SANDOR LORAND, M.D.

I

The knowledge of the dynamics of psychotherapy is derived from the psychoanalytical study of the problems which underlie every neurosis. Infantile experiences and unconscious repression are responsible for early formation of the neuroses. Whether we are doing psychoanalysis or analytically oriented psychotherapy the procedure is the same, namely, an uncovering process. The difference lies in what we uncover and what we want to uncover. What we do in psychoanalysis and what we do in psychotherapy is, in this regard, different. Naturally, in psychoanalysis we strive to obtain the whole pathology of the patient; the psychoanalytic process is really a reconstructive history-taking.

In psychotherapy, analytically oriented or dynamically oriented, one also obtains the pathology, but usually *not the complete* pathology. In this instance, we have to rely on many things. We have to know in advance, or at least have a good intuition concerning what may be the problem to be un-covered, and more so, we must have in advance some plan as to how far to uncover and what to leave undisturbed. In analysis, as you know, this is usually not the case. In psycho-therapy, this uncovering process is the same as in analysis, but it is not the same in degree or in approach to the manner of uncovering.

Another thing shared by both psychoanalysis and psycho-therapy is the theory with which you approach the patient. You have to have a theoretical understanding of the patient's prob-lem right from the beginning. Naturally, when you sit and talk with the patient you form an idea about what the patient suffers from and what the problems may be. Suppose, just as a simple example, the patient has a phobia of lightning and thunder. Whether you want it or not, whether it will be right or not, you will develop a theory of your own which you want to prove. In the process of therapy, the patient proves whether your theory is right or wrong. Approaching the patient with your own theory is something which you must have in both techniques. In analysis, you can postpone ideas longer because you can have proof by waiting for it a longer time. Psycho-therapy is more difficult than psychoanalysis and more compli-cated. You must have more rapidly organized thought and some concept of what to look for and in what direction you want to progress, in order to approach the basic problems and alleviate or reduce the conflicts of the patient more rapidly than in psychoanalysis, even if the effect may not be perma-nent.

Reduction of the patient's conflicts, if not elimination of them, and making the patient more tolerant towards frustra-tion and able to live with himself, is naturally the final aim of any psychotherapy, including analytic psychotherapy. But, again, it is a more difficult process in psychotherapy. Your task is to achieve this aim more rapidly, in a shorter, less round-about manner. In accomplishing this, you should be aware, from the very beginning, that your problem is really to strengthen the patient's ego. All the problems you deal with— unconscious problems, superego and id problems—all come down to dealing with the patient's ego which is weakened by many aspects of life. It is weakened because of adherence to attitudes of childhood, childhood fixations, dependence, and an inability to face adult reality. So, the problem of ego weakness and ego strength is of importance, in your psychotherapeutic approach, from the very beginning, just as it is in analysis. It is important in both to be aware, from the start, of how much the patient's ego will be able to tolerate, how much it will sustain him, and how much understanding to give and in what way this can be accomplished. You have to know the patient's strengths and weaknesses. You will decide this from impressions gained in the consultation and from the patient's history. You will also have other ways to judge this for yourself. You will consider, as you do in analysis, the duration of the neurotic difficulties, the chronicity of the illness, and the age of the patient, in order to know how far and how deep to go. Tolerance is related to the ego strength and elasticity of the patient.

Let us now consider the problem of the therapeutic process. Creating an acceptable milieu for the patient is accomplished by the conscious or unconscious assistance of transference relationships. This, again, is a more difficult problem in psychotherapy, where you have to be very careful to avoid a full-fledged transference relationship. Only in deep analysis can you permit that. In order to maintain the ego strength of the patient and keep it mobile, so as not to make the patient too dependent and too involved and cause too much regression in the therapy, you must manage the transference—the intensified transference which occurs in therapy, the positive and the negative transference. We must also consider, in therapy, the fear of transference and transference resistance. Transference is what mobilizes the whole process of therapy. Transference can become a problem and to handle it you really have to know where you are going and where it may lead you. It can become a great avenue on which you travel to achieve the most with the patient. It can also become a very difficult process which bogs down and spoils the whole aspect of therapy. You may be aware of this when the patient misses appointments, doesn't want to come anymore or doesn't want to talk during the sessions. That is transference resistance. The transference itself may become a resistance through negative feelings which at times you may counteract with the right interpretation. When resistance does come up, let the patient externalize it and then try to redirect it in psychotherapy to where it belongs. You may let it go on for a little while until you can interpret it. The patient may develop what appears to be a strong transference and may want to remain in that transference relationship. In psychotherapy, this appears often and the therapist may even help it along and foster it. The patient's ego weakness, ego dependence, anxieties, phobias, all may serve the purpose of being dependent. Transference may become a source of resistance and you cannot make any progress unless you have the ways and means to reduce it.

Transference may also function as resistance in that the patient does not want to express or show it. He is afraid of getting attached, of getting involved. The negative therapeutic reactions reveal this state of affairs very clearly. The resistance then serves the aim of preventing movement. The patient wants to remain dependent. The therapist may inadvertently help him develop this dependence and reliance so that he does not move. When the patient does not want to express or show the transference, he does not want to accept anything, because he does not want to become dependent. He is afraid of that dependence which covers many aspects of his personality and his problems. This transference is important from the standpoint of therapeutic manipulation. The interpretation of the positive or the negative transference is important, though with the positive transference it is less so, unless it goes very deep or becomes erotic. If so, you have to be careful, because in psychotherapy, one should not permit it to go so deep. The negative aspects of transference, when the patient is aggressive and negativistic, are much easier to handle in psychotherapy. You can immediately connect it with his reality situation.

In psychotherapy, there is always movement around the patient's environment, mainly his close family. From there, you may branch out as far as the patient leads you or as far as you want to go. How far to go, where to stop, and what level to maintain are important. The patient may try to seduce you into going deeper and material will be revealed which you may find you cannot readily handle. You have to formulate your own theory, your working hypothesis, with which to operate. What you expect in the patient and what comes forth indicates to you how to keep at certain levels so as to avoid going too deep or becoming very involved. Another reason why the transference manipulation is important is the regressive tendencies of the patient. In psychoanalysis, the whole problem of regression is a very complicated one. It is not just that the regression is a defense reaction of the patient. It is more than just that. It is biological and constitutional. We all regress in our dreams and fantasies. Patients use it mostly as a defense, in the therapeutic process, and will utilize it especially when transference manifestations are strong and dependency on the therapist is great. Transference dependence leads, then, to attempts to repeat situations again and again, as the whole neurotic process is a repetition of patterns of earlier life. The regressive process may become very strong and you have to be very careful. That is why we talk about the depth of therapy, i.e., "how far to go."

You must also consider the problem of how much to permit the patient to act out before you interpret or show him what he is doing. How far you let him regress, how much you let him act out in the therapeutic process, how much you let him act out outside the therapy, and how much you direct him to act out in his environment are of great importance. All this is related to the problems of transference. Permission for regression is also our concern. Unless you have proper theoretical working principles at the beginning and know the patient's weaknesses and strength, and his tendencies to withdrawal, to depend or to be guided properly, you may easily get into trouble. If the patient regresses too far, he may then have a prepsychotic or psychotic episode. With some patients, you can judge in advance whether or not therapy may lead to a psychotic episode. This is also not infrequent in analysis.

In my collected essays (Lorand, 1950), I described such a patient. This patient experienced a psychotic episode for two weeks and then continued further therapy. He needed that episode. The patient's father was told in advance: "You have to realize that in the course of analysis your son may develop a psychotic episode and will have to be hospitalized." After three years, while the analyst was on vacation, the boy did have a psychotic episode. He continued in analysis for about two more years and is now successful in his profession. You have to anticipate this kind of thing in advance so that you are prepared. You can learn about patients who have a strong tendency to regress from their history.

The three important discoveries of Freud are: the unconscious, and the roads leading to it; repression; and the origin of conflict in earliest childhood.

Repression is associated with regression and the level to which the patient regresses. Appraisal of ego strength and weakness will be based on the functioning of the ego, as well as the patient's history and current situation. In order to appraise the ego function, we certainly have to pay attention to the patient's productions from the beginning. We have to consider the patient's thinking, feelings and action. What are these and how does he express them? This will be important for an appraisal of terminating therapy. Consider the patient's confusion in these areas. Parallel to this is the relation to another triad: anxiety, aggression and guilt; remembering these factors will help you in your therapeutic work. These six principles—feelings, thinking, action, anxiety, aggression, and guilt—are the ones with which you work, in psychotherapy.

What the patient thinks, what he feels, and how he acts gives you the working theory. If the patient is very anxious, you already know that he has equally strong aggression, either unconscious or repressed. If there is anxiety, there may be aggression against a person or situation which causes the suffering. If there is repressed aggression, there is unconscious guilt. In reference to unconscious guilt feelings, we know that the patient is not aware of them. He is only aware of anxiety. For instance, he may be afraid of lightning and thunder. He crawls under the bed or pulls down the window blinds. He does not know what he is afraid of. He knows that it is childish. It is very simple to connect this with guilt, and fear of being punished. This is guilt one feels for doing something wrong. Unconscious guilt is experienced for unconscious hostility or aggression. You see how these three are related. On a more superficial level, the patient talks of anxiety and you know from your theory that this patient is also aggressive and feels guilty. In order to gradually relieve him of anxiety, one has to reach his understanding and show him that he has anxiety because there is something else behind it, something that will have to be ventilated.

We will not go back to infancy to determine how feelings, thinking, and action develop. Action comes on the basis of thinking and feeling. But in the case we are considering, there is great confusion in the patient. What the patient really shows is that he is dependent and that he cannot act. Why can't he do anything? Because if he acts this out it may make him anxious and aggressive or it may make him act in a way that will make him feel guilty. Paralysis of action is very common in neuroses. What paralyzes the person? Actually he does not dare to act, he does not dare to feel and he does not dare to think. When the patient says, "I cannot act," you ask "why?" Thus, it will lead to other sources. Thinking and feeling in the neuroses are considered, by the patient, to be identical with actions. This is where the guilt arises. Just like children, they feel that they will be punished for their thoughts and feelings, so they have to repress them. Here is where regression originates. They are saying: "I cannot act. I'm a helpless child. If I cannot act I will be taken care of."

As early as 1920, Freud focused attention on the problem of ego strength and ego analysis in connection with the structure of the personality (id, ego and superego). Remember to put the ego in the middle. If the ego is to be strengthened, the superego has to be weakened. Now, if the patient who is afraid of lightning and thunder, is afraid of God's punishment, it means he offended God somehow and feels guilty. Here we have a religious implication. There are also parental figures against whom he has, or had, rebellious thoughts and feelings. He has to learn not to be afraid of this superego figure. Eventually he will not be afraid of other forces inside himself. Conflict will thus be diminished and, because every neurosis is a result of conflict, the neurosis will be reduced. You have to manipulate the six principles previously described.

Let us recall the classical example of the girl who thought she had killed her mother. Her mother had died of cancer. The girl had taken care of the mother for months. She gave her medicine, and had had to come home from the office to do that. When the mother finally died, the girl thought that she had given her too much medicine and thus killed her.

She felt very guilty and depressed. Her fear that she would die or go crazy was cleared up in three sessions. The fear cleared up, not her whole neuroses. In our discussion of the whole affair, I drew attention to the fact that she had had to come home every day for months just to give medicine to mother and then had stayed home for the evening. I asked her:

"Were you very active before that?" Answer: "Yes, very active." "How was your social life?" "Very active." "How was it during the time of the illness?" "I did not see my friends, I did not see anybody." "Did you ever think," she was asked, "about mother's death and how it would be if mother would die?" "I talked to the doctor about it. The doctor said it would be much better for her to die, and I thought it would be better for her." "Now, how do you feel about that?" "The doctor said it would be better." When her mother finally died, all the early childhood ramifications of death wishes against the mother arose. The thought that she killed mother came up. She was intelligent and understood. She also recognized that she must have thought of her mother's death often, because she felt so frustrated and was forced to keep away from her friends.

Concerning frustration, the patient's ego has to be strengthened so he can tolerate frustration. You don't cure a patient in psychotherapy. You help a patient to live better with himself; tolerate frustration better; be less depressed; be less afraid of his superego and inner feelings; and to be less afraid of reality. So, we consider the toleration of frustration which is directly connected with ego strength. Making the patient's ego stronger helps him in tolerating and understanding reality, as well as his frustrations and anxieties.

How about the patient's symptoms? Here, we can discuss patterns. You know how symptoms originate, as well as their economy and aims. There are at least three aims connected with every symptom. One is to get some attention, to be able to depend, to have somebody eliminate frustration. For example, if a child has a (symptomatic) bellyache, he is kept from going to school. But he also feels guilty because he has cheated and he knows he did something wrong (this is what happens with neuroses and what causes trouble). So, with a symptom, there is always guilt and, at the same time, there is also an expiation of the guilt. While the patient has the symptom, through which he wants to accomplish something, he also feels guilty because he has cheated. He wears a mask, so to speak, feels guilty, and he has to punish himself. The symptom makes him suffer. (This is clearly observable in obsessional neuroses and in hysterics.) He feels that he won't be punished more severely if he punishes himself. The symptom is also a *denial* that he did or thought something wrong. It is as if the patient with anxiety is saying, "It's not true I'm aggressive. I don't wish harm to anybody. I'm a poor helpless creature ridden with anxiety. I'm busy with my own anxiety. How can I be busy being aggressive toward anyone?" These aims have to be clarified for the patient, if you want to make his symptoms less.

Positive transference itself may remove the symptom for awhile. You take care of him and absolve him from all guilt, help him, guide him, hold his hand, and lead him; at which time he may lose the symptoms. Through the symptoms, he has gotten what he wants. You have to be aware of these implications in neurotic symptom formation (wish fulfillment, defense, atonement).

Regression means going back, but it also expresses resistance against going forward or growing up. The patient sometimes says, "I go one foot forward but I slip back two." Sometimes we tell him that he slipped back three, in order to push him further forward. Going back, getting away—this is always a defense against the anxiety of growing up. It is important to consider this type of anxiety, in psychotherapy. That is why we talk about fixation points going back to somewhere in the past. Regression has not yet been sufficiently clarified. How far do we permit the patient to regress, if at all? Do we allow acting out? How can we stop regression?

Regression can best be studied through dreams. Every dream is regressive. Dreams have to be considered in psychotherapy; they are still the royal road to the unconscious. If you know dreams and understand them, you know where the conflict lies. The most expressive regressive dreams may guide you in orienting yourself clinically and deciding what you have to do and how far you can go. Regressive tendencies act mainly as resistance.

Fear is always of unconscious drives and the superego, the world outside, and criticism. For example take the agrophobic or claustrophobic patient and see why he does not want to go out. You will find out how it serves him as protection. The regression protects one from the anxiety one does not want to expose one's self to. In the phobias, this is seen very clearly. With childish behavior, you have to know how much regression to permit, where to stop it, and when to pull the patient forward. If the patient is pushed forward against anxiety, there is the matter of acting out. How should he act, and how would you advise him to act, in certain situations?

Let me quote another clinical example: A depressed and anxious girl, who, on her job, made constant mistakes in typewriting and stenography, came in for therapy. She was afraid that she would be fired and nobody else would employ her. She got drunk and she feared losing her mind. She was unable to concentrate. In a short while, within weeks, it was learned that her condition had begun after Christmas. The other girls were given a raise. She was the boss's stenographer. She did not get a raise, so she began to hate the job. She was angry at the boss and was jealous of the other girls. She soon realized that whenever the boss dictated to her she made many mistakes. She corrected them on the typewriter but she was still not sure whether they were right. The letters were given back to her. The boss was very patient. She retyped each letter three or four times. She was asked, in therapy, "Did you ever think what you would like to do about this?" She said, "I cannot stay on the job. I have to look for another job, but if I look for another job, who will give me a recommendation? I won't get any from this job. I'm not so sure of getting another job. It is difficult to get another job." I asked, "What else could you do?" She said, "Maybe I could talk to the boss." She was asked, "Why don't you?" She then went to the boss and he told her that she had not gotten the raise because she was going to get one in June. At first, when she did not get the raise, she had thought to herself that she would like to throw the whole job at his head. This was the clue that led us to the cause of her hatred of the job.

So you see, there is acting out in a positive way and a constructive way. It would not have helped to tell the patient to tell the boss off. Rather, she was advised to go *talk* to him. So, you advise the patient to communicate and work the problem out.

The therapist has to have an idea, a theory, that he works with. He should know what he wants to do about the problems the patient presents. He has an idea about the patient's problems and realizes that there is always regression to previous behavior. It may refer to father, mother, and childhood. He is right, because the patient himself says that his behavior is childish and he is ashamed of this. After the first few interviews with the patient, we have some ideas about the dynamics, what's going on inside, the immediate conflict, and how to plan for therapy. In psychotherapy, you cannot just go on as in psychoanalysis. The whole analytical process is history-taking, to an extent. You analyze, interpret, etc. If you know your theory, you can visualize what you want to do with the patient. You must consider the chronicity of the illness, the reason for the illness, and ego strength and weakness. You have to crystalize what you expect to do and what you would like to accomplish. If you understand the ego strength you will know how much it will be possible to accomplish and how far to go in therapy. If you see the road is difficult, you may be satisfied with less. In order to have an idea of what you want to do, you must make some dynamic formulation. This dynamic formulation is correlated with the factors of anxiety, aggression, and guilt, and the problems of thinking, feeling, and action. Some concept of what the patient experiences, in his confused state, is required. You have to know what causes his depression, whom he hates, where the regression is anchored, etc., and what the therapist must do to dislodge it. If the patient is suicidal, will suicide be discussed, uncovered, or hidden? It should not be hidden. One should talk about it. The more you talk about the patient's suicidal tendencies, the surer you will be of getting somewhere with that patient.

What are the possibilities that the patient will change in the environment in which he lives? What are the possibilities that the patient will change outside of that environment? This is important, because problems concerning environment always become involved in the problems of the patient. How far can you go in trying to ease the environmental pressures? The possibilities of the patient changing, in the present environment, and how much can the environment itself change, have always to be considered.

A knowledge of psychodynamics may aid you in anticipating a psychotic reaction, possibly deeper depression or hypomanic reactions. You have to depend on judgment, intuition and knowledge. Psychodynamic diagnosis enables you to estimate the depth of the patient's problems and the profundity of the patient's involvement. You may be able to predict how the course of therapy will proceed in a positive way and you may be able to judge what may happen negatively and thus be prepared. You must be on guard and not promise much. You may say, "We'll see. A great deal depends on you, on the situation, and on what you can handle. If you cooperate you will get more out of therapy," and so on. Always be conservative about promises. A good policy is "Watch and wait." As mentioned previously, manipulation of the transference actually means manipulation of the patient. When we ask the patient to externalize his problems, we say: "What could you do? What will you do? Let us see the possibilities." Encourage the patient to proceed with discussion of the possibilities of action. Sometimes, manipulating the environment will also be possible. Manipulation of the environment is, in some cases, a necessity. One purpose of planning the therapy in advance is to decide, from the early history and some understanding of the whole problem, how much you can hope to accomplish. It is most important to plan the therapy in the beginning.

The result of therapy depends greatly on the severity and chronicity of the illness, the age of the patient, the susceptibility of the patient to therapy, his desire for therapy, the personality of the therapist, and the preference of the therapist for the treatment of certain types of cases. There are certain cases you like and certain cases you do not like. It is preferable to avoid those you do not like to treat. Do not try to be a conqueror. Some therapists do not treat depressions. Every neurotic is depressed, but some therapists do not treat deep depressions. They may prefer hysterical cases, they make like to treat sexual difficulties. Some like young patients who can be manipulated better and quicker. If you have preferences in therapy, you may have better results with them. Preference is related to the therapist's personality. Eventually, we all tend to become selective.

DISCUSSION

Question: You used the phrase "manipulation of transference." Will you amplify it?

A remark from one of the participants: You seemed to play down the libidinal aspect.

Answer: We just mentioned the manipulation of transference and its involvements. This covers the libidinal aspects. Now, by manipulation I mean first, acting—telling the patient to go out and handle some of the problems discussed and clarified, relying on the therapist, knowing that what was suggested may succeed. So we lead the patient. This is one aspect. But there is more to manipulation of transference when it comes to aggressive, negative transference and positive, dependent transference. In psychotherapy, when the patient will call you names, you will have to manipulate not to let the patient get in so deeply that you become a personal target for his aggression, even for the time of the therapeutic session. The patient may have an emotional outburst, be angry—do not allow it to become the usual process by saying: "Express your feelings about me." Don't encourage it! This is manipulating transference. Stop the patient and interpret. The same with sexual transference. If the patient brings too many sexual dreams and fantasies concerning you, you must realize that you should not go into them deeply. You say: "You have those thoughts, feelings and dreams because you are a sexual being and you have repressed too much. You have such needs and you talk to me about your problems. So you have some thoughts about me, not just dependence, but dependence for gratification of some drives. You know very well that it is not me whom you want in reality." Don't go into it deeply. One may say: "You have to be attached to somebody, to depend on somebody, be taken care of in every respect, even in your love life. You know very well that we are here for therapy and that wouldn't do." Some therapists put their wife's, or husband's, picture on the desk. That's also a good way. The patient may say, "Who is that ugly woman there? How can you love her? Why not me?" So the problem of manipulating transference means dealing with the patient's aggressive and sexual dependence. You have to manipulate this and you have to think about it carefully and calculate how much curiosity and how much narcissistic gratification there is in it. The patient may like you too much and expect too much. How far do you let it go? This type of transference may cause trouble to the psychotherapist.

Question: In the reference to analytic psychotherapy, I have the impression that you are involved in a kind of patchwork therapy. If you deal with younger people who have recurrences and you keep on patchworking your therapy without digging into the underlying childhood neurosis to the best of your ability, then what happens, for example, when these individuals reach their menopause and experience a worse condition?

Answer: What do you mean by patchwork therapy? Do you mean doing therapy from time to time? Do you mean that the patient comes back again and again?

Question: With relapses, are you looking for elimination of symptoms plus a reorganization?

Answer: In therapy, we refer constantly to infantile, earlier patterns. I use this scheme. When the patient says: "Doctor, I cannot think," I say: "Certainly you can. You think all day. You are merely saying you cannot think. You are confused about thinking, deciding, now that you are here. Is it because you want someone to think for you? But don't you think that is the early pattern of your childhood, of papa and mama thinking for you and wanting them to take care of you?" This is how one behaves in childhood.

Question: But do they have the time and opportunity to work it out?

Answer: They always have the opportunity, because they come for a period of time. In those cases we have cited, a short-term therapy was required to eliminate the main disturbing conflict. We did not cure them of their neuroses or of their underlying personality difficulties. We merely used them as an example to show how, by understanding the problem and externalizing the patient's point of view, you can reduce the symptom. That doesn't mean that you have eliminated the symptom completely and reorganized the patient's personality. Now concerning what will happen later, you have to depend on many things and hope. To illustrate, I have some older patients in psychotherapy. One of them came twice a week for about two years, then once a week for a year. After that, she did not come for a while because of other difficulties. Nevertheless, she managed fairly well with her family. She returned, somewhat depressed because of external circumstances. She now comes once a week to discuss various actual problems. She is not seen more than that. She gets medication and I discuss her problems with her. She does some volunteer work, which she never wanted to do before, and has even increased the time and frequency she gives to it, lately. She has a better social life. We discuss matters and it makes her more comfortable. I have another man, not a young one, who has been coming for years. He was seen once a week, twice a week, then not at all for three months. He came back again to discuss external actual problems in his life. This is always connected with patterns of his childhood. We do not quit. It has been going on for years and we don't reorganize his personality. You must help them to adjust to getting old and accept it gracefully. A woman who just recently came back, after many years absence, has problems and says: "What's the use, I am getting old." But now, she, too, is learning to adjust more gracefully to old age and to accept it.

Question: Dr. Lorand, you said that one must know the age of the patient and the chronicity of the illness in order to estimate and plan the progress in therapy. Do you mean the results you can accomplish? Do you mean that you set your goals in therapy? When, in the course of therapy, do you consider setting the goals of therapy? Is it after a period of trial therapy, early in the treatment, or as you progress?

Answer: All of your questions cannot be answered categorically, but, generally, there are certain indications which you may take into consideration concerning the goal and possible results of therapy. Take for instance the problem of age. It is natural that a younger patient is more elastic, will be more amenable to therapy than a chronically ill, aged patient. You can very well imagine that a young person with depressive moods will be able to gain more, and quicker, from therapy than an old chronically depressed person. This also implies, to an extent, the goal of the therapy. I may want to bring about more improvement in the younger person and I may accomplish it, whereas, with the older person, I am less interested in refreshing and reviving old problems which resulted in the patient's sickness. This type of goal-setting may be considered after a few months of therapy, when we know all or many of the ramifications of the patient's symptomatology and also his mental ability or ego strength to stand frustration, to try to counteract reality difficulties, and to compromise and handle his environmental problems more elastically.

Question: I gather, Dr. Lorand, that you give your patients plenty of leeway and allow them to determine how frequently to appear for therapy. How do you know whether this constitutes an essential need or resistance and how do you differentiate that from patchwork therapy?

Question from Dr. Lorand: On whose part, the therapist's or the patient's?

Answer from the participant: On the therapist's part—or both.

Answer: Naturally, both the patient and the therapist may have resistance. The therapist's resistance goes under the heading of countertransference. Whether to treat the patient in frequent sessions, or less frequently, depends on the personality of the patient, his symptoms and the involvements of his symptoms, and the chronicity of his illness. All that may create resistance in the therapist to frequent sessions. There may also be resistance from the patient to frequent sessions, for many reasons: environment, previous experiences, certain fears being acutely involved from the beginning of therapy, fear of what his symptoms and neurotic problems may do to him, fear of becoming very dependent on his therapist, and, among other factors, the financial situation. In addition, my experience over many years has been that the majority of patients got along pretty well in nonfrequent sessions— though, in the beginning of their therapy, for a few months, they may have been coming twice or three times a week. However, very soon they reduced the sessions from twice to once a week, or even once every two weeks. At times, I left it up to them to call me for an appointment after a long period of absence, whenever there was something they wanted to discuss.

After many years, when the patient is sufficiently improved to make the decisions, then he may call only when a difficult problem arises.

As to the question, "Do I consider all this patchwork therapy?" Frankly, I believe the type of psychotherapy which we are discussing here tonight may be called "patchwork" by some. You are not remaking the personality or reorganizing the dynamic structure, you are just modifying it here and there, and sometimes patches help. Patches will last for a long time and will make it possible for the individual to function for years to come. Naturally, that does not imply that the therapist is just a patchworker. Psychotherapy is a very difficult process, more difficult at times and with some patients, than psychoanalysis proper. That is why you have to acquire fundamental knowledge and feelings about dynamics, what you intend to do with them and what you are doing with them. You are consciously manipulating—willingly or, at times, unwillingly.

Question: Dr. Lorand, I have been conspiring with some of our colleagues to pop this question. I didn't hear any mention of the term "insight" in your lecture tonight. Are you evading it?

Answer: I am certainly not avoiding the term "insight." It is implicit in all I have been talking about tonight and in other sessions on psychotherapy. The whole of psychotherapy, or analysis, is insight, gaining insight through therapy. The therapist is equipped to have insight from the beginning and is constantly gaining insight into individual cases through therapy.

If you give suggestions or directions to the patients, you do so because you have insight into his condition and the working of his mind and emotions, and you know fairly well that he will be able to follow, at least to a degree, your suggestions and advice.

You aim to help him, strengthen his ego, and to weaken the at-times all powerful superego. How can you strengthen the ego, weaken the superego, and bring them to harmonious functioning, if you have no proper insight into the workings, antagonisms and contradictions between the two?

To re-educate the patient means you must have insight, understand him, and have a proper estimation and appreciation of his transference manifestations, difficulties, and involvements.

Even your interpretation, which you consider an important agent in your therapy, has to be based on your insight of the patient's understanding, so that he can appreciate your interpretations and accept them, based on his own production of material which substantiates the correctness of interpretation.

Consider, again, the example of the girl who made typing mistakes and was afraid that she would be fired by her boss. In the course of her therapeutic interviews, it was found that she was really afraid of the boss because he might criticize her for the mistakes that she was making. On the next level of understanding, her insight showed her that she was really angry at the boss and that she did not care to do good work because she did not get a raise. So, her mistakes were really the result of an unconscious desire to get even with the boss and annoy him. At the same time, she created guilt feelings and a need for the punishment of being dismissed. After all that was discussed with her, she understood it very well, but continued to make mistakes. She still hesitated to go in to see the boss with the letters she typed. The patient said to me, "I understand it all. I know it all." She had acquired intellectual insight, but had not yet acquired—shall we say—the emotional insight necessary to manage her problem. Shortly after discussing her problem on an intellectual level and referring to the various feelings which she had at this period in relationship to her work, changing her job, her colleagues and friends in the office, the boss, and her fears and aggressions, I suggested she try to talk to the boss and tell him why she was disturbed. The patient did this, with good results. She acquired her own

opinions, feelings, evaluation of the whole situation, and cour-
age, and this was the real insight, intellectual and emotional,
which made her less afraid to act.

II

In Part I, I covered fourteen topics. First, I talked about
psychotherapy as an uncovering process. Then I discussed elements of theory, such as when to start and when to stop therapy.
I touched upon the aims of therapy, ego strength and ego weakness. I spoke of therapeutic milieu, progress of therapy, transference and how it develops, the important role of regression,
resistance, resistance in transference, and manipulating transference. I talked, too, about the importance of thinking, feelings and action, as well as anxiety, aggression and guilt. Finally, I discussed frustration, the meaning of symptoms and the
dynamic formulation of the case material. It was a most complicated lecture, for a most complicated subject. Of course, this
is a year's material in one lecture. It was an attempt to stir
you to think about and organize all the aspects of the therapeutic process.

Now, let me attempt further differentiation and clarifica-
tion. I gave you six factors: feeling, thinking, and action; anxiety, aggression, and guilt. Let us see what the basic difference
is between psychoanalysis and general psychotherapy. It is very
simple and lies in the dynamic approach *versus* the structural
approach. In psychoanalysis, we work with the dynamic approach. We try to reduce the pathogenic charges of the case
on the basis of dynamic structures, that is, ego strength, ego
weakness, conflicts which exist between the instincts and the
ego, the superego and reality, and so on. In psychotherapy, we
take into consideration the personality structure and we try
to strengthen the ego or the different parts of the personality

against psychogenic charges without entering too deeply into the depths of dynamic conflicts.

In psychoanalysis, we consider the pathogenic charges through a dynamic understanding of the case. We study the dynamics and what goes on in the different parts of the personality. We try to reduce those charges which are pathogenic. In psychotherapy, we do the opposite. We take the structure of the personality and we try to strengthen it to withstand the pathogenic charges. The difference is a bit deep and subtle, but the mechanism is not the same, and though the goals are the same—help the patient—the aim and method of approach are different. Unfortunately, psychotherapy has no established theoretical basis for the various types of treatment. There is no coherent theory of psychotherapy. At one time, it was taught—and Freud also mentioned this—that there are two main varieties of psychotherapy. One is psychoanalysis, which I refer to as dynamic, and the other is suggestive psychotherapy. This means that all nonpsychoanalytic psychotherapies are founded upon suggestion, while psychoanalysis is not. However, Freud, himself, talked of it later, and you know how much suggestion, re-education, etc., do enter into analysis. In practice, it must be recognized that while psychoanalysis is not free of suggestion, it makes every effort to minimize suggestion, manipulation, impression and guidance, all of which are the essence of psychotherapy.

How shall we teach psychotherapy? We know how to teach psychoanalysis to some extent, but there are differences there too. A variety of teachers have different ideas and approaches. We know, for instance, that the teaching of psychoanalysis is done by imparting knowledge in clinical conferences and in supervisory analysis. The personal analysis is a very useful teaching instrument. It is analysis, which is therapeutic to a certain extent. It is also teaching, naturally, because, in any psychotherapy, you assist the patient in learning different kinds of behavior and different types of morals and ethics. In psychoanalysis, instruction consists of supervision and clinical conferences. Perhaps we can learn from psychoanalysis, which is a type of psychotherapy, and impart knowledge through the means of clinical conferences and supervision. This approach, I believe, is the ideal teaching method for psychotherapy. You present clinical cases and hold discussions of these cases. In these clinical conferences, there are expressions of opinion about the various approaches and manipulations by the various psychotherapists. This and supervision of cases undergoing therapy are desirable.

We will not discuss clinical conferences at length because this is clearly the heart of medical teaching. Several people take a case and discuss it. When everybody expresses himself, you gather some ideas and conclusions as to who did better work with which approach and who had better results. It is possible that this might demonstrate that one may obtain the same results by different methods of manipulation. Such clinical conferences are an important source of learning, since you impart knowledge from your experiences and obtain knowledge from other colleagues; you crystalize ideas and you think about the next person's contribution just as you think about your own.

Supervisory learning is a more difficult problem because here one person supervises and imparts his knowledge to you. He seeks to indoctrinate you with his own theory, whereas you, treating the case, may have your own opinion and a different approach. It may be a better approach for you than that recommended by your supervisor. This can happen and has happened. The problem then rests with your ability to express and carry out your own ideas in a way your supervisor learns to accept. If you only look with awe at your supervisor then you accept his remarks as gospel. I shall relate to you what can be an actual experience. In various hospitals and universities, the residents are supervised by the most senior members of the staff. One doctor may thus have three supervisors. The three supervisors will each implant different ideas and show different ways of handling problems. This can be good, because the resident learns different methods of approach. If he has some stability he then develops his own views and method. However, through inexperience, he may be troubled by multiple approaches and actually not know which to follow. For instance, should he accept the advice recommending he sit and say nothing until the patient talks and then chime in or should he follow the advice to interpret everything right away? Should he follow the suggestion that he should not interpret or should he listen to the supervisor who tells him "not to interpret dreams except superficially"? As the patient produces material, should he try to amalgamate it and use what he can for his own insight or should he follow the one who says "You wait and listen and get the patient's associations and then do interpretation, as one does in analysis"? As supervisors are not always analytically trained, and neither is the resident, confusion develops.

Should the resident be told that, in psychotherapy, you must wait for associations, though he does not know how to analyze them? Then he is already in trouble! This is also true in connection with dreams, which he will be unable to analyze until he has had proper training and experience. When one supervisor says, "You interpret everything" and another supervisor says, "Sit back and don't interpret, be passive and wait for months if necessary," there will be trouble. It is inevitable that the young doctor will lose his patient if he does not know what to do. The patient will just walk out and believe that psychiatry cannot help him.

The supervisor may say, "Make quick, short, concise interpretations and that's all. If you do not, it indicates that you are not certain about what you want to say." Certainly, the psychiatrist may not be sure what he wants to say, but it may be a sign of even greater uncertainty to make short, concise interpretations. I believe that that type of supervision is wrong, because the patient will not understand. Short interpretations are useful, at times, to a patient who is in analysis for three-to-four years. He is experienced and already knows what he said and is therefore capable of catching it himself. In psychotherapy, even in analytical psychotherapy, you have to carefully formulate and clarify (see Lorand, 1946). I have emphasized how important interpretation is, how important the language of interpretation is, how important the timing of interpretation is, and how important the tone of the analyst's voice is to the patient because interpretation is always taken as a criticism and a threat. The patient is given a reasonably concise interpretation in language that is not scientific and that is on his level, so that he can understand it.

How can a patient utilize interpretation if you don't first educate him so that he can understand the meaning of his illness. He will say "What has this to do with these other ramifications of my problem?" However, with the patient in analysis you can say, "You talk about the mayor of the city! You know what the mayor of the city is, always papa." The analytical patient will understand that, because he has gained the proper background in his three-to-four years, which enables him to recognize that all superior figures are a symbol of papa. He can accept this short interpretation. But for a psychotherapeutic patient, who has been in treatment only a few months or a year, the same interpretation is sheer nonsense. This is why you have to develop your own impressions when you see the patient and tell the supervisor, "Look here, doctor, I don't think I can give a short interpretation to this patient. I don't even know how to give a short interpretation." Of course you can say many things, though I would rather the patient said it first so that I can be sure it was not planted in his mind. What one should learn is not to give short random interpretations but, rather, interpretations which the patient understands. I don't believe any psychotherapist should limit himself to short interpretations, because if he gets accustomed to that and is very stingy with words, he will antagonize the patient. Patients do not like stingy therapists, not even stingy analysts. They want to get something and when you don't talk they are annoyed. They may say, "At least if *you* don't change my mode of living, tell me how *I* should do it." All this means that you have to think a great deal about the problem of supervision. You supervise the patient and you are supervised by a supervisor. The problem should not become one of "who supervises whom."

Now, all psychotherapists, all analysts, all supervisors, are not infallible. Therefore, we cannot rely entirely on one training supervisor. In analysis, you have two or three supervisors; the analysand will learn something from each one and, with a few years of experience, he will learn more on his own. In consulting analyst-supervisors, it must be recognized that many analysts do not like psychotherapy and they admit it. They prefer not to do psychotherapy and, so, may not be adept at it. Psychotherapy is at times more difficult than psychoanalysis, for the simple reason that in psychotherapy some patients are more inclined to hold the therapist entirely responsible. Obviously, in psychotherapy, the doctor must more actively guide the patient and, at times, interfere with his reality functioning, as well as manipulate the environment. In analysis, one keeps one's self free of that. Many analysts won't see the patient's parents and others won't even see the husband. The husband frequently does not like it, because he pays for the analysis and feels he has the right to be seen. In psychotherapy, you cannot function that way, though some young psychotherapists try to avoid this responsibility. They try to manipulate the patient as if the patient were in analysis and it does not work. The patient sometimes leaves and they then phone the patient to learn how he is and to try to get him back. I don't blame the doctor for calling the patient. It is nice to call the patient and ask, "What are you doing? Do you want to come back?" There is nothing wrong with that. However, it is a ticklish problem which some analysts do not like and, therefore, they avoid doing psychotherapy. They are not comfortable with so much talking and confrontation.

You are expected to prescribe medication for the patient; that, too, is your responsibility in psychotherapy. You have to talk to the family when this area becomes involved. As I said before, in psychotherapy you interfere with a patient, you give advice, you take more responsibility, and you therefore have to know more and be more elastic. But, in psychotherapy, you have an advantage. You don't sit around so much. One of my patients in psychotherapy said to me, "The doctor sat on the table, cleaned his nails, smoked a cigar and then he made himself tea and drank it." I said, "At least did he give you a cup of tea?" He said, "No." I said, "You did right in leaving him." And I meant it! This psychotherapist's behavior was offensive. If a supervisory analysand were in my office, I would offer him a cup of coffee if I had one myself. In the case I mentioned, it was more than the patient could tolerate and more interference than the psychotherapist intended. He had frustrated the patient too much.

Not long ago, I spoke of training and the various types of technical approaches before a new society. We talked about frustration and analysts having to keep the patient in a state of frustration. I said, "It's not necessary. An analyst should understand that being in analysis, by itself, is enough frustration for the patient." Transference provides considerable frustration, as does the problem of talking and not talking. Why add to it? I mentioned the patient who was so frustrated by the doctor who didn't serve him tea that he left him. They agreed it served the doctor right.

As to the problem of dreams, if a patient is with a therapist for about a year, or longer, and it is felt that the therapist knows enough and is working satisfactorily with the patient, the supervisor may suggest that for the next few months all that he bring him is the patient's dreams, so that he may observe how he uses dream material. The supervisor can then learn whether he knows where the patient is.

I think that what I have written about analytic interpretation is all valid for psychotherapeutic interpretation. Since language must be clear to the patient, no scientific terms should be used. I can offer a clinical example. I have a patient at present who thinks she is in analysis, though she is not. I told her that. She is in analytical psychotherapy. She comes three times a week and produces dreams which she never analyzes. She adds ideas to them so that when I try to analyze she rejects and laughs about it, saying, "What help is that in my situation?" She had gone to a psychoanalyst and then a psychotherapist for awhile. This woman has one important problem; she has a strong tendency toward nymphomania. As a young girl, she chose to have a nose operation although she had a perfect nose. Interestingly, she told me that she first went to a surgeon who said to her, "You know what I will do? I will hire you to sit in my office so you can tell everybody that your nose was done by me." She had such a perfect nose that he wouldn't touch it. He sensed her trouble was something else. She went to another country to have her nose operated on. Now the problem of her nose always comes up when some trouble arises or when a man drops her. Everything is "my nose, the ugly scar, and my nose, nose, nose." Her second therapist, an analytically oriented person who had been in analysis, also told her, "So much is connected with the nose. The whole problem of castration." She could now tell me that her nose represented a penis and that is why she ran after men and that's why she has all her trouble. He was right, naturally—it has a great deal to do with her problem. But she never really accepted it and she doesn't actually understand it. This shows the problem of language and interpretation with this patient. She left this therapist after a while. She'll leave me, too, because I am making her face her actions. She asked, "What does that do to me; why do you tell me that, what do you think, doctor. Why can't I get married?" I replied, "You tell me why can't you." She doesn't like it. I don't give her all the reasons and I make her work. To an extent, she likes coming, because, since coming, she weighs a little more, thinks more seriously, and is in better harmony with her family. She doesn't like the situation that she has to come. I won't change her hours at her request. Her time is not strict, at least not in my opinion, so she will soon leave me also. She has had two vacations; for one I let her go, for the other I charged her. She didn't like that. She wants to know why she can't go for ten days or so and not be charged, etc.

Consideration of her nose problem is important for our purposes and serves as an example of why one does not give an interpretation which scientifically and analytically may be correct. It is one thing for you to know and another thing for the patient to know. Here, we face the patient's language, understanding, and attitude. She knew that the nose operation was castration; she calls it that, and she laughs. But when she is miserable, she says, "Still there must be some reason why I put everything on the poor nose." I said, "Because this is what everybody sees and you look in the mirror and you see it and you always kick yourself and think 'why was I operated on.'" It develops that it had a great deal to do with her mother and brother. It was a spiteful thing also. So she is miserable. Here, we see active interference and an interpretation of active interference. It depends on what you interpret, how you interpret, and when you interpret.

All this presents a useful and important example for learning, if you can discuss it in clinical conferences or in seminars. You are asked what you told her and what happened, as a result, the next week. You tell what happened. Then the next doctor will say, "I would do that and that," and the next will say, "I did that and that." This is how you will learn, not what to do, but rather, what not to do.

I also find, in psychotherapy, that the patient is told at great length about the symptom, the meaning of the symptom, and the symptom-formation. Naturally, we know very well that it is important that the patient should learn gradually about the use of the symptom. In psychotherapy, when you explain the meaning of the symptom to the patient, during the first few months it gives him some advantage. Then you explain the economic aspect of it, the infantile repetition-pattern. It is a problem for the therapist to really know at what time, at what length, and how, to demonstrate it for the patient. You cannot ever demonstrate it unless you have the keys. You have the opportunity to get the key in the patient's actions, in the use of symptoms which he brings to you. For instance, a girl will have an anxiety spell when she goes to get a job. She is tried out on the typewriter. Any time she feels like writing a letter or sits in the waiting room until she is called in, she gets a pain in her fingers and a cramp. After she tries a few times, the cramp disappears when she begins to type. Now this is an important time to say to the girl, "Now look here, let's discuss that. What happened in the waiting room and what happened when you went in and wrote the letter?" You make the patient understand that you have to have the material. In this manner, you may get material the next time she comes. She will tell you that she did so-and-so in order to achieve this or that. Then you explain the whole psychodynamics and you are in a position in which you can work with it most effectively. For instance, I again refer to the patient with the nose problem. That patient got the interpretation of the symptom and its ramifications without being prepared or having some understanding of it. By connecting the whole thing with the sexual aspect, certainly she had to reject it.

To repeat, how one explains the problem of symptom formation is of vital importance in therapy. In the psychotherapeutic process, the patient will produce new symptoms. You may want to explain that on the basis of the transference, which can be absolutely wrong in psychotherapy. Besides, in psychotherapy it is certainly wrong to say, "You developed this in order not to come, or to show me that I don't help you." When the patient is not ready for it and you do not have that deep understanding of the patient or the patient is openly resistant, it is wrong to interpret. Suppose you give medicine to the patient and she says, "Yes, I took the medicine but I felt much worse afterwards." You may say, "What did I give you? Why did you feel worse?" You tell her what you gave her and why. Then you say, "Perhaps that had something to do with it, that is, wanting medicine from me, but, at the same time, showing me that my medicine does not help and maybe you thought of going to another doctor?" When you point this out, sometimes you will find that the patient had in mind, "Maybe I should go to somebody else to get better medicine." Sometimes the patient will go to a good family doctor and get some medicine, a placebo, and that will help. This type of situation offers a good opportunity for the appraisal of transference reactions, which you can learn only by experience. Then, when you meet the situation you can understand it and use it therapeutically.

For instance, a patient had been in analytical psychotherapy for a long time, having had a depression for years. She was operated on, but for some time the details of her experience were not really discussed although we talked about them at times. Being in psychotherapy and meeting three times a week, still did not permit covering this matter. She then suggested it and we talked about it. She accused the doctors of performing unnecessary operations because she wanted them. She had not been able to bring this up before, even during a three-year period of previous psychotherapy. How one presents, to the patient, the problem of her body image depends on anticipating what will occur if this is done. She discusses her nose and I am very careful about when to talk about it. When she brings it up and she is miserable, I let her talk and we talk about everything else but sex. Why is the nose a problem and why does it drive men away? I never suggest that she wants a man. She may come to this matter herself. The self-punishment aspect of the symptom is very important. To explain this to her theoretically is also wrong. The patient has to come upon it and realize her masochistic need, the need to suffer. Then you may say that perhaps she wanted the symptom and she may realize that she wanted all kinds of illnesses, and then you again have difficulties. She may feel that she does not want the symptom for punishment, that even an amputation would be preferable to the symptom she has, and she may deny that she needs it for punishment. One must not argue with the patient. That is wrong. The punishment aspect is very difficult to explain and difficult for the patient to comprehend.

Because psychotherapy is an exploratory, digging up, excavating process (as in analysis), designed to make the unconscious partially conscious, you have to be very careful what you leave repressed. It is often better to leave things buried or repressed than to merely touch upon them. Dreams are the royal road to the unconscious. We understand what is going on, with the help of the dreams, if the patient's conscious reporting doesn't bring enough material. One must learn to deal with dreams. Another question is that of the advisability of asking for dreams. A patient, who was analyzed for about eight years by somebody else, has been with me for over a year and has brought very few dreams. There is so much turmoil and upheaval with the conscious material and so much to discuss regarding its ramifications that we have not yet arrived at dealing with dreams. But it is unavoidable at some period in therapy. Patients will bring a dream or will even need a dream to know what is going on. To understand a dream is one thing; what to do with it is another thing.

What do we understand about the dream? To understand dreams is to understand unconscious conflicts and the pathology, which will also indicate the progress of therapy. There is both the manifest and latent meaning to comprehend. I shall give you two examples. A patient brings in two dreams that

occurred the same night: "I walked with mother. Mother said
that she left the two pussy cats at home and I said to mother,
'Oh, mother, how could you do that?' I felt that mother was
cruel." The same night she had another dream, following that
dream: "Father is deriding me that I am too fat. I say to father
it is none of his business and I berate him." I did nothing, because the patient brought out the interpretations immediately
by means of her association. Why did she dream of pussy cats?
What did the pussy cats represent? You have to understand
symbolism to know what the pussy cats represent to the
patient. "The female, the female genitals, breasts?" That's
very good so far! What else? "The pussy cats represents
mother leaving home." "Siblings?" "The cats are female, but
also male." It is interesting that the patient said, "Mother used
to call me the big pussy and brother little pussy cat." But I
knew that anyhow, without the patient telling me, because I
knew the patient—that is manifest in the dream content as I
read it. I knew immediately that the patient referred to a cruel
mother—you know that—and that is very important. Then
you can talk to her about the cruelty of her mother and the
fact that she loved her mother very much and imitated the
mother ideal. She wants to be like her mother and we talked
of the cruelty of her mother in childhood and how, in early
childhood, when her brother was born, she felt great frustration and a great deal of aggression against both mother and
father. She recognized her feeling toward her father, but did
not realize her feeling toward mother and viewed her as cruel.
Further association revealed that the mother had visited the
grandmother and left the children at home. At times, she was
angry toward her grandmother and not her mother. She was
spiteful toward the grandmother.

The problem of her father in the dream is very simple. She
was really not afraid of her father and, also, her sexual ideas
are quite different from what they were before. The father
always watching her weight means that she knows "father" has

incestuous significance, because the father told her that "if you were not my daughter, I'd bait you." She had fantasies of pregnancy with the father; she had dreams in which she had illegitimate children whom she brought home to father, and then told the father, "The child is not legitimate because uncle so-and-so is the father." When you have two dreams like that and you know your patient and your patient's problems, unavoidably, you have to understand something of the dream, even without association. If you ask for associations and they are as clear as this, you have no trouble. However, associations may go deep and if you construct interpretations that do not hit the target, you may not do harm but neither are you doing good. It is important how much association you elicit in psychotherapy and what part of it you utilize, but if you have an understanding of the manifest dream contents, you can see that it fits in. You may ask questions if you wish, but you should connect the material with what the patient has already produced. You may say, "You know the dream refers to the unconscious and that those dreams and fantasies refer to what you have told me." You don't have to interpret everything. You interpret only what is fitting and propitious. In psychotherapy, it is important to recognize this, because this is where you can get into trouble. When considering transference and interpretation of transference on the basis of the unconscious content of dream materials, in psychotherapy, one must be very cautious, because that may take you deep down to where you don't want to go.

If you want to give guidance or do superficial therapy and not exploratory or deep therapy, the problem of time and duration of therapy arises. In making arrangements for therapy, there are certain ideas to follow, depending on how long the patient is to come and on your goal. In analysis, the goal is to make provision for better functioning and happiness by improving tolerance to frustration, tolerance of reality, and improving sexuality. But, in psychotherapy, one must know in the beginning what he *wants* to do, how far he wants to go, how much he wants to destroy and build up again, and how much he *can* do. This is also important in connection with dreams, because interpretation leads to greater depths and the temptation to go deeper and deeper. Then the patient regresses and there arises the problem of how to bring him back and how to terminate. You may behave, consciously or unconsciously, in a manner which leads the patient to leave you when you want the patient to leave; but the patient should not feel abandoned. You may have to find other patients to replace the one who leaves and you may have conflicts about this, as well as knowing from the beginning how far you want to go, and for how long, and you should not be unhappy that the patient leaves you, etc.

I say that the dream is a clinical indicator of what is going on in the patient, because, through the patient's dream, you will see how deep the conflict goes and how much the unconscious is still resisting. The clinical importance of the dream material is in the confrontation with the unconscious. You have the dream material to assist with understanding and you can say to the patient, "Look, in the dream you are constantly running away, but consciously you are constantly challenging somebody or vice versa. What do you want to do?" This is the utilization of the dream material, i.e., confrontation with the unconscious material of wishes, desires, and drives, in the presence of a conscious attitude. This is where the therapeutic value enters. You don't have to take a flower pot and throw it at his head—just tell it to him nicely. This is how to utilize the knowledge of the dream for therapeutic purposes. This is an important technical approach, the technique of handling the material and the patient by understanding unconscious material through dream production and then confronting him. In analysis, this is a part of "working through." Working through is always confrontation; what the patient is doing and why he is doing it. You combine the whole thing, but always keep it superficial, supporting it with the material that you have gathered. This is the theoretical explanation of the clinical processes.

In starting psychotherapy, I let the patient talk. Naturally, the first sessions are mainly history taking. Don't forget that all psychotherapy, just like psychoanalysis, is history taking and dealing with history. So long as the patient comes, you are reconstructing history, always starting with something new that you use in connection with the old. I let the patient talk and then I ask many questions. I may start the questioning from the top, from the present situation, or I may inquire further into the past, concerning friends, occupation, attitudes, and schooling. I ask all that and many other things. It depends on how talkative the patient is and on the patient's symptomatology. If the patient is a phobic patient or an anxious patient, I won't ask many questions, just those pertaining to the phobia and anxiety. There, I start with greater reassurance and explanation on a surface level. The fears, childish, adult, reality, and imaginary all require reassurance. Starting therapy cannot be answered theoretically. It depends on the patient and the conditions. When you see anxious patients, or character difficulties, you do not start in the same way. In a character case, you might explain the resistance early—why the patient doesn't want to feel—and you may go into theory. If he is intelligent, the patient may understand it. In depression, you start quite differently. Let me repeat, again, that the starting procedure of therapy depends on the patient, his character, and his symptomatology. These have to give you the lead.

Finally, how do you terminate therapy? When are you satisfied that the patient functions better? I never terminate therapy by telling the patient he is completely well. I say instead, "Look here, you are doing pretty well on your own. Try a bit more on your own without coming here. I am always here and you can always call and come back if need be. Give yourself a few months." To terminate treatment, the therapist must know the difference between the patient's functioning now and when he first came. There also remains the problem of assessing the gains and liabilities, and pointing these out to the patient in terms of what has happened since he came. He may hesitate, and feel that this is not enough, but you suggest that he try to continue on his own. There is no set rule as to how to start and how to terminate treament. You have to use your clinical judgment (derived from training and experience) to decide when you are satisfied with the patient's progress in treatment. Sometimes, the patient would like to come forever and you should not permit this. The time should be made flexible so that appointments can be spaced so as to lead to termination and separation.

III

I have stated previously that all types of psychotherapy employ six factors. When you work with one, you also affect the other five. If you encounter guilt or anxiety you must question what creates it. If you consider when to terminate therapy, you must note whether, in those six areas, the patient is functioning differently than when he first came to see you. To what degree he functions depends on how well the patient has worked with you. Termination will depend on whether you are satisfied enough to let the patient go out on his own and utilize his revised values, in accordance with those six factors. This is the same as with analysis. I stated that the aim of psychotherapy is to have the patient function better in all the fields in which he has to function, i.e., in the social, pleasure and work spheres. To what degree there is improvement depends on the patient's potential and, naturally, on his ego strength and ego weakness. One must determine to what extent one can help the ego to function differently and when the patient is ready to start on his own with new insight and new capabilities. Therefore, the decision for termination depends on what was originally your goal in therapy—how far did you want to go, how much did you have to strengthen the ego and reduce inhibitions. You evaluate how far you will be able to go, and when the time comes that you reach that aim to some satisfactory degree, you can let the patient go on his own.

When is the patient ready? In general, when he functions better in his work life, his social life, and his pleasure life. This involves being able to tolerate frustration better than he did when he first came for therapy. It means less anxiety and being able to see that life is a difficult process; to withstand and manage the pressures to an extent that incapacity is avoided. The toleration of frustration is an important factor, as is the patient's insight as to what he used his symptoms for. In other words, when the patient is ready not to use symptoms for the "economic" purpose of gaining attention, evading reality, and for self-punishment, he may be ready to terminate therapy because he has sufficient insight to live even with symptoms. The patient now must have a realization of what his symptoms meant to him and the realization of what the symptoms will mean in the future. This is the meaning of toleration of frustration. This is why you have to talk to the patient about symptoms. If they were neurotic, as for instance, conversion hysterical symptoms and psychosomatic symptoms, he must know what he utilized them for formerly and how he wants to use them in the future. If he uses them, he should be aware that he uses them, and for what purpose. He destroys, in other words, the unconscious mechanism of symptom formation and a relief from symptoms may follow. We have talked, quite at length, about the indications of insight, conflict, the strength of the conflict and the changes of the conflict from the unconscious to conscious.

Investigating dream material is also important in the problem of termination. Before the termination, for a time, we see that the patient's unconscious conflicts are different than they were at the start. If the patient, for instance, is suffering from sexual difficulty, you may find at first that dreams show, in their manifest content, that sex is dangerous, and the wish in the dream may be expressed in running away. In the course of therapy, when the patient learns more, gains more insight, and obtains more support and understanding, you may see in the dream a new tendency, the wish to change, and sex will appear less dangerous. The patient also constantly tries to improve in his social life and, especially, his work life. You will see that the dreams are not so regressive. If the patient has a strong transference, then the dreams may continue in their regressive aims. This, also, is a warning as to how much you let the transference develop and how deep it becomes. If you don't treat the transference, there is always a tendency to deep regression because the patient always wants the therapist to make up for every type of frustration of the past.

The dream is also an indication of where you are, from the standpoint of termination. Naturally, all these matters concerning when and how to terminate will also depend on the type of neurosis involved. In the various neuroses, there are various indications from the patient's point of view and your own. This refers to anxiety hysteria, conversion hysteria and character neuroses. In character neuroses, where the patient's main symptomatology is problems of behavior, we have another problem in psychotherapy, namely, how to make the patient realize and have some feelings and sensations and not be afraid of his emotions. In this case, the therapy and termination are different.

Yet another problem is the termination of therapy with the obsessive compulsives: how much do we change the type? We make the obsessions or compulsions milder or we replace them. There is not much more that one can do with obsessive-compulsive patients. At best, one can only change the character and the intensity of the symptom. The obsessive character will always be an obsessive character; the compulsive neurotic will always be compulsive.

When does one terminate the treatment of a patient with an obsessive-compulsive neurosis, who presents the special problem of how far to go, how much to change the compulsions? When is one to be satisfied with the result? Surely the patient has to be satisfied and able to tolerate his frustrations and compulsiveness. The aim is not to "cure" but to help him withstand anxiety, accept reality, and accept himself and his remaining symptoms.

This last section is concerned with the types of dynamic psychotherapies and their use with various types of patients. There are many frames of reference by which the various psychotherapies are characterized. First I will mention "supportive psychotherapy," which is the most common type generally used. "Supportive" means holding the patient's hand and giving him all the support possible, from every aspect, with medication, explanation, guidance, restriction, and changing routine. One patient, for instance, now has a routine which does not interfere with her functioning. She is doing hospital work, voluntarily. I have discussed matters with her and she develops some projects for herself as to what to do socially. This is simple supportive psychotherapy.

Next, we mention "suppressive psychotherapy." Here, you teach the patient to suppress and *not* to think of the problem or unpleasant thoughts. The outstanding examples of this are suggestive and hypnotic psychotherapy. These are predominantly suppressive. The suggestive type of therapy should first be suppressive to an extent, but later has to be more supportive and more cathartic. You do not explain very much, but when the hypnotic therapy is over, you tell the patient to continue psychotherapy to deal with his conflicts. You discuss as much as you want to, and bring forth material when the patient is in a state where he can take it, i.e., not so phobic, anxious or agitated. That would be one of the suppressive methods. In "cathartic psychotherapy," the patient externalizes conflicts. He also externalizes certain feelings in the transference, but you redirect them to where they belong. You let the patient talk to you about his environment and the people in the environment with whom he is disturbed. The catharsis will then concern feelings which the patient would not have thought of, or had not thought of before, concerning parents, siblings or perhaps the work situation and social situations.

This simpler type of psychotherapy can become complicated. It depends on what you do. Do you want to remain on the surface or do you want to lead the patient deeper (which then means that you will meet stronger transference problems, which you have to be ready to deal with)? Naturally, you will utilize the transference situation in determining the course of therapy. If you know the patient is very dependent and attached, you will point out that this is a pattern which relates to the problems of his past.

Successful psychotherapy also implies success with what follows therapy. The patient may come back to you at times and you let him come back. He is thus maintained by the transference. If the patient makes excessive demands for your intercession with his problems, then you must explain that this is not one of your functions. You may say that you can only give him a mirror to look into, but that he will have to look and do something about it for himself. At times you have to interfere to a degree and lead the patient.

We now come to the matter of the duration of therapy. This also depends on all the factors we have discussed. Certainly, it depends on whether the treatment is superficial or deep. It is a good idea to anticipate how long you will go on with the patient and how often you will see him. The patient will ask how long he must come. Certainly you can't say exactly how long, but you can say he will come until he feels better and is able to manage things better, without depending on you to tell him what to do. Fractional therapy enables you to terminate. Let him come for awhile, a year or two, or six months, and then let the patient be on his own and come back again if necessary. This is much better, from my point of view, because you will never give the patient a completely satisfactory resolution of his conflicts and make him perfectly well and forever satisfied. However, you can help the patient to feel better, to accept limitations, to a degree, and then let him try to get along on his own. Though the patient at times comes back, that in no way means he did not do well in psychotherapy. Sometimes, I see patients I saw twenty years ago. They come back when they get into some new difficulty and need additional help.

In all these therapies which are considered suggestive, you are the authority, you are the new representative, a new superego. The patient wants you to take over his life and change the world around him. The patient has to be made to understand that you cannot change the world but you can change him to some extent, enabling him to look at the world differently, and then he can change, bit by bit, the little world around him. This means that his feelings toward his work situation, pleasure situation, and social situation have to be modified. You must be aware that you are the authority for the patient and you have to know what is desirable for him. You have to know how to manipulate, how much to make the patient understand, in what way to use your authority, and in what way not to use it.

Supportive therapy is usually used like the suppressive type. You suppress the symptoms. You try not to talk about them too much, because from the moment you begin to do so, you destroy the suppression. With suppression, the patient does not feel anxious. You encourage suppression because you know intuitively that the suppressive and supportive therapy will result in relief for the weak ego. That's why you also leave the symptoms out of the discussions as much as you can. You must talk some—how much is up to you—because once you actively go into symptoms you have to proceed deeper; this raises the question of how much the patient can tolerate and how much sicker will he become. In analysis, it is very proper, but there you see the patient every day. When such a patient develops new symptoms you are prepared and have the time to deal with them.

The second category, in the group of therapies, would be abreaction therapy. That is a type of expressive psychotherapy which brings in many problems. How far do you permit expressive abreaction? It is not just confession. When the patient confesses, it is already somewhat therapeutic, as you know, and is what the church accomplishes. It is not free association, but it is of some use. The patient talks about things more easily when he confesses. However, the confession in therapy always involves something deeper. In his associations, the patient certainly reveals more and that leads to a deeper transference relationship, which requires a greater need for interpretation. Of course, you may stop him and give an interpretation in connection with the material produced rather than in the direction of abreaction. Let the patient talk, but redirect associations concerning feelings and thoughts to the immediate environment, instead of working with it on the basis of transference. This is again a matter of choice, which cannot be taught by lectures. You have to possess a feeling for it. Only in clinical conferences can you see, by discussing cases, how you got into deep water or how you could have stayed out. The next time the situation occurs, you may automatically stay out, since this becomes one of the ramifications that one now senses automatically. You, the leader, the superego, must take charge to the extent that you know what you want to do. Here, we come back to what we talked about at the beginning, the aim of psychotherapy, i.e., what you want to do, how much can you do, and how much will the patient tolerate.

For example, a patient came twice and I saw that she was

unable to talk. She sat still and let me talk and attempt to draw her out. How long could I talk of her parents, her trip to Paris, her husband and social life? She did this twice and then I said, "Now, look here, you don't want to talk. You are also taking medication, so maybe you feel well. What do you want to do? Maybe you don't want to come. Think a little about that. How would it be if you came only one evening or suppose you phone when you want to see me and I will always give you an appointment." "Oh, no doctor," she said, "you think once a week would be all right?" I thought she probably wouldn't come once a week either. "Oh, no doctor," she said, "that I wouldn't do, you know I want to come, I must come." Her husband was very happy when she came only once a week because it cost less. You test the situation and determine what you want to do. The monetary factor may be important at times.

Now let us come back again to the duration of treatment. It is up to you and the patient, but mostly up to you, because the doctor is the superego and the patient is in need of him. You can usually influence a patient to come as often as you feel necessary. There are many problems that influence frequency. For example, the patient comes to you for psychotherapy, two or three times a week, for a long time. What do you talk about? The patient may not have much to say twice a week and, even after a long time, only gives you a report of what happened during the week. Then you have to talk and you have to have the energy and willingness to talk. When you talk very much and you have to force it and don't know quite what to discuss, it makes you tired and then *you* will need the psychotherapy and that is not so good. This is why I think interrupting the therapy at times and telling the patient to try on his own has an additional advantage. Let the patient try to be on his own and tell him he can always come back. Many patients appreciate that. Others will say, "You are sending me away, you don't want to see me." It is only when the patient understands that the door is always open, and he can always call or come, that he will feel safe. You also do this for your own protection, as well as for the patient.

Expressive therapy is often, in acute cases, very helpful. The patient is agitated and very anxious and you have to reassure him. You cannot say, "But this is all childish and we won't talk about it." Let the patient express his feelings and abreact, then you interpret. His fears, aggressions, and sadness subside when he brings out his feelings, and interpretation gives reassurance.

Naturally, all the therapies that I have mentioned can be organized as you want them. Whatever is done in psychotherapy is done in the interest of the patient. In psychotherapy, you often have to say to the patient, "I give you the suggestion, suppose you think about it."

For instance, take an adult patient who does not socialize and is afraid to go out or go on vacation because she feels nobody will like her. She does not know how to make contact with people. She would like to, but is afraid. You suggest that she think about what will happen if she does go out. Will she be rejected and have a miserable time? What will happen if she does not go? Will she feel miserable sitting home? You say, "You are miserable anyhow, so which will you choose? Suppose you do go and you feel miserable? What will happen?" This is a very good approach, that every psychotherapist should use, because this is the way to make the patient feel and think on his own. You might say, "Suppose you did go, what would happen?" "Oh," she says, "I can't go with my friend. She'll have a date and I won't have a date and I will be miserable." "All right," you say, "then what will you do? Or what can you do if you feel miserable?" "Oh, I could sit in my room and mope." "All right. What else could you do?" "Yes, I didn't think of it. I could go home." "Certainly you could go home. You never thought of it. It is obvious that you can get a bus. There are other ways, you can get a taxi and then come home. So what's the difference?" So she goes and has a good time. That is how she learns.

Take the case of a patient with angioneurotic edema, who wanted to go to Honolulu. But why go far away when she is afraid of flying? She had a dream that before she went a shark bit off one of her legs. She came to me and told me that in the dream she showed me that she was still dancing well on one leg. She was still afraid to go. So we talked about the whole problem. I said, "You have the whole summer. What do you want to do?" She said, "Oh, New York will be terrible. If I go to the country with my mother it will be terrible." "So what will you do in Honolulu?" I asked. She replied, "But I don't know anybody there." I remarked, "But your father told you he has business contacts there." This is how you work out what could happen. If she flies to Honolulu, she has to transfer at San Francisco. She has many friends there. "Suppose you don't feel better in Honolulu and are tired after a week. What will you do?" I asked. "I could always come back to Los Angeles or San Francisco, I have very good friends there," she said. "Certainly you can," I responded. So she went and she had a good summer.

It isn't always this way; there are disappointments. However, this is interference again and forced fantasies. You should never neglect this in psychotherapy. Yet, you cannot just go on forcing fantasies. You do not put the ideas in the mind of the patient in all decisions. You let him work it out, but you have to participate actively. In psychotherapy, you are always influencing the patient in a more direct manner.

We come again to the problem of termination. In psychoanalysis, termination depends on what the patient decides. You agree, but you cannot say that you don't interfere. If, when the patient says, "I will leave this spring," you answer, "All right, we will talk about it," and you ask, "Why in the spring? Is there anything else that comes to your mind," you are influencing the patient. In psychotherapy, you have to influence even more directly. The patient may tell you he wants to leave you and be on his own. You can tell the patient it is time to go, or time to stay, or time to come back. You cannot just leave it up in the air and have the patient come and come. Sometimes you have to make him leave.

You try to externalize the patient's thoughts, organize them, interpret them, and then decide with the patient. The patient can only decide what to do under your influence and your suggestion. It comes as your advice and the patient then decides whether to follow it. However, don't let the patient simply think or decide impulsively. In my opinion, psychotherapy consists of doing things for the patient more directly. I can't see that there is place for direct frustration in psychotherapy. It is enough that the patient has to learn to tolerate frustration. You should not add to it. There is much you can do for the patient; certainly you have to give more than in psychoanalysis. I have done psychotherapy and psychoanalysis for many years; I see the difference pretty well and I clearly establish the differences for myself, right from the beginning of treatment. I counsel the patient in psychotherapy; I don't do this in analysis, except in a roundabout way by interpreting. In psychotherapy you re-educate the patient more directly. It is the job of the psychotherapist to counsel, to educate, to suggest, and to interpret.

I left "interpretation" for last, because there is an important difference in its use, from my point of view, in analysis and analytical or direct psychotherapy. I don't interpret in the beginning. I first elaborate on the production and see what it means to the patient and what the aim may be that is behind the verbalization. Then, if I want to interpret, I always interpret in terms of the ego. For example, if the patient talks about dependence, advice, direction, I may say, "You want me to be your parent, you understand that I'm not your parent. You want me to teach you, to guide you, etc. You know this is childish dependence."

In psychotherapy, interpretation can be given only when the patient is ready and knows the early pattern which is responsible for his present behavior. Premature interpretation is not such a harmless thing. In psychotherapy, some practitioners say to start interpretation right away. The patient says something and you interpret. Now, the question is what does interpretation mean to you and what does it mean to the patient? When you elaborate something to help the patient understand his production and behavior, this is also interpretation. But, by interpretation, you always refer to something unconscious. I refer here to the situation in which the patient does not know what was the basis of a dream or a slip of the tongue, and you interpret it. This is a different type of interpretation. That's what I mean by not waiting for the patient's associations to the dream and elaboration of thought. Interpretation, elaboration, all produce material to make the patient understand more. The situation is put to the patient, not as a direct interpretation or admonition, but as a question, perhaps. The patient understands it; he understands that what you say always refers back to the material he talks about.

How do we actually terminate? You could initiate termination by saying to the patient, "Look, you have come here long enough. I see you are doing things fairly well on your own. Go on with work and then you will see how you function." You prepare patients to expect termination and discuss with them their reaction to being on their own. You cannot just say, "This is when we terminate," and dismiss the patient.

DISCUSSION

Question: Prior to termination, what are some of the aspects to keep in mind in notifying the patient that you are going on vacation?

Answer: Naturally, you go for a vacation and the patient goes for one also. We discuss it openly. No definite attitudes are necessary. At times, I let them take several days vacation and don't charge them. If patients in psychotherapy stay away at times I let them go for awhile.

Sometimes a patient calls and says he cannot come because the alarm didn't go off and so he cannot arrive on time. What does he want to tell me; that he will come tomorrow instead or that he will keep his next appointment? I tell him to come even if he will be late. Five minutes later, the patient may call and say he'll skip breakfast and hurry over. Another type of patient is the one who has to go to the dentist and cannot come. In one actual case, the patient's dentist was going to Europe and he had no other time to see him. The patient could not come because he must have time for the dentist. I said, "Think about it, you want to see the dentist because he treats your teeth. Why don't you want to see me? You think about it!" He thought about whether he really could not come. His appointment was available and I didn't give him a new appointment. If he really could not come and his tooth had to be attended to, then nothing could be done about it. Otherwise, he calls and comes in. If the patient cannot come in, what do you do then? It depends on the patient and on your attitude— on the patient's progress, and on your recognizing what it means to him. Sometimes, one does not mind if the patient is defiant, a little daring. Sometimes one does not mind the patient feeling a bit guilty. In psychotherapy, he gets away with many things. I am a very lenient type of psychotherapist. I look upon patients as children, so they get away with things at times.

Patients in psychotherapy can go for a vacation at any time. Analysis patients can go only when I go or, if they cannot go then, I let them go at a specified time. However, everything is discussed on many occasions and I must know that they have no other time. Psychotherapy patients are not interfered with so strictly. If I let one patient go for a week's vacation, I don't charge him, but I do warn him that I may not have time when he comes back. Don't be rigid. You cannot act as you would in daily sessions analysis. Certain patients who go for vacation at odd times are told that I will charge them. I won't charge for some of those hours which I will use for myself. At times, it pays to let a patient go for a short vacation and not charge him. This can be a good experience for the patient.

Years of experience have taught me that there is an advantage to utilizing any type of problem in therapy. I think the patient should know, and also expect, that when he goes for a vacation he has to account for the hour, since I cannot keep the hour open. He certainly is entitled to know that you charge for the hour when you hold the hour open. That's why analysts are entitled to be paid and patients are charged for the hour. I don't charge a patient when he is sick medically or when something unpredictable and unavoidable prevents him from coming.

The psychotherapist is, in a sense, a person who is born to do psychotherapy, though there are attitudes which at present can be learned. These are inherent in the personality and appear in the form of attitudes and a sense of deep empathy. There is no exact uniformity to this. You see this in the many types of psychotherapy and different approaches now used. Everybody develops special approaches. You may like certain types of cases because you are good with them. You may not like other types because you are not so good with them. You may refuse such cases and send them to somebody else.

Question: How would you handle a case you have seen once a week for several months, where the patient suddenly says he can't afford to come for the next month because of unusual expenses?

Answer: I continue to see them and tell them to pay me some day when they have the money.

Question: What has been your experience in getting paid?

Answer: I usually get paid. I never have a fixed fee. I never refuse to see the patient in consultation. I have quite a consultation practice which does not pay. I never refuse a doctor.

The doctor will ask, at times, what you charge and will say the patient cannot pay. I say, "I will see your patient anyhow, for whatever fee he can pay." I may see the patient only fifteen minutes and, in that time, I can tell whether the patient needs therapy and what type, and then I send him to someone else. I may say, "You know what your trouble is, but I think you should go to a clinic if you can't pay." I can always find time for any patient a doctor sends to me or for any doctor that comes to me for consultation.

However, I don't believe that doctors should give their services free to people who *can* pay. I take care of money matters and I tell my patients from the start not to be ashamed or shy about discussing money problems. I don't send bills by mail; patients get the bills from me. I give them the bills to encourage them to talk about money matters. I never saw a patient who didn't have difficulties discussing money matters. We know that money represents power, security, etc., and a great deal of libido is invested in the handling of money. Also a great deal of frustration and insecurity is bound up with money problems. The problems which money creates are directly connected with the patient's ability to "get" and "give" —"resentment" and "love"—and with his reality functioning.

BIBLIOGRAPHY

Lorand, S. (1946), *Technique of Psychoanalytic Therapy*. New York: International Universities Press.
——— (1950), *Clinical Studies in Psychoanalysis*. New York: International Universities Press.

Child Psychiatry and the Adult Personality[1]

RICHARD M. SILBERSTEIN, M.D.

When I was asked to discuss some subjects of my own choosing, in the area of child psychiatry, I had an idea that it might be worthwhile for me to review the multiple factors influencing the human personality as it proceeds from conception through adolescence.

I have since, however, chatted with many friends, who are members of the Society, all of whom have warned me that you are well-versed in psychoanalytic principles and that most of you have also been obliged to learn the vicissitudes of the development of the libido for your Boards and for your teaching activities. Each of these conversations contained an implied warning: Don't go over the old stuff they all know—tell them something new. As my friends spoke to me in this way, I became concerned, since child psychiatry is a field which lacks a basic organization. Child psychiatry has no universally accepted

---

[1] This paper, prepared for listeners rather than readers, was designed to provoke discussion and thought rather than to convey ideas necessarily embraced by the author. It should be read with this in mind.

authoritative scientific journal, no simple classification of diseases, and no effective, universally accepted standards of the average, normal or expected. Adult psychiatry shares some of these difficulties. Adult psychiatry, however, seems to have at least passed through its preschool phases so that one psychiatrist can speak to a colleague in another part of the country, with some degree of authority and assurance that a common point of view can be found. They can agree on such basic matters as the nature of a defect in reality testing, the meaning of the mental status examination, and the adequacy of an examination of the sensorium. In these very basic areas, child psychiatrists cannot agree even concerning the interpretation of a simple mental status examination. Two children, demonstrating the same type of mental status to examination, might be suffering from one of the many varieties of ego disturbance which are classified as psychoses, they might be suffering from lack of human contact of the variety described by Spitz (1947), which he termed hospitalism or anaclitic depression, or, then again, they might be simple mental defectives. When the available history fails to give us the leads and the clues necessary to the understanding of the mental status examination, we sometimes cannot make the proper diagnosis.

In addition, there is a multitude of workers, in the field of child psychiatry, whose work has not been coordinated or synthesized sufficiently to weld their individual contributions into a realistic whole. Thus, Sigmund Freud, Anna Freud, Arnold Gesell, Jean Piaget, and other outstanding contributors to the field of child psychiatry, worked in similar areas and made valuable contributions, but the nature of these contributions have never been incorporated into a common point of view. The contributions of sociology, anthropology, and clinical psychology have been numerous, but independent, and it is a rare child psychiatrist who has incorporated the latest thinking of each field into his own frame of reference. I will not, however, belabor the deficiencies of the field I must discuss with you. Instead, I will attempt to synthesize for you some of the contributions child psychiatry can make to the understanding of adult behavior and to illustrate the clinical importance of recent research in child psychiatry. I will report, therefore, on areas of current interest in child psychiatry, with an attempt to synthesize rather than criticize. I am reporting the ideas and opinions of others, not necessarily my own.

Let me ask you to give up your sophistication for now and allow yourselves to think of one of your patients, of one of your friends, of one of your children or perhaps, even, of yourself. Let us return this person of whom we are thinking to a time prior to birth, prior even to conception, and consider some of the phenomena which have contributed to his present construction, personality and nature.

Probably the most understood aspects of his present nature deal with his heredity. We would probably all agree that his intelligence, his physical health or familial disease, the nature of his stamina, and the nature of his beauty or ugliness would all relate to his heredity and would all have an effect on his present personality and present position in society. Certainly, if he is handsome, he finds life easier than if he is ugly and if he has much stamina he finds life easier than if he is lacking in energy. If he is bright, his position in life is different than if he is dull. His race, of course, is also determined by heredity. In this day of desegregation, surely his psychology is influenced by his race and the color of his skin. Some authorities would tell us that the weakness or strength of his various body organs are also determined on a hereditary basis. If the person you have chosen to follow through this discussion is a person with a psychosomatic disease, the nature of his stomach trouble, his lung disease, his gastrointestinal disease, or his hypertension is said by some to be predetermined by heredity.

Perhaps less obviously, but of great importance to a psychiatrist, the strength or weakness of his instinctual drives is determined on a hereditary basis, and drives are of an organic

nature and subject to the vicissitudes of heredity. The person
who has demonstrated this most clearly is Margaret Fries,[2] in
her work on activity and passivity. Her movies vividly demonstrate the completely different activity patterns of newborn infants, from wiry, vigorous, energetic children requiring little
stimulation from the environment to passive, sluggish, and
placid babies requiring much stimulation from outside if they
are to participate even in the basic act of feeding. Talent, or
lack of talent, physical size, perhaps even temperament, are
determined by heredity. I mention these few illustrations only
to remind you of the multiple contributions of heredity to the
nature of the personality of your adult patient.

Assuming that we now have a view of his heredity, let us
review just a few of the congenital influences in his life. Obviously, the presence of disease in the mother during gestation,
such as syphilis, rubella in the first trimester, or diabetes, would
have an influence on your patient's physical structure and on
his personality and thinking. The state of nutrition of his
mother would also influence the type of person that he is.
Children whose mothers had a diet poor in protein are said to
have less well-developed facial bones than children whose
mothers had an adequate protein intake. Even the status of
the mother's emotional health is said to influence personality
structure. Phyllis Greenacre (1952) suggests to us that mothers
who are more anxious tend to have children who are more
hyperactive. Mothers who are emotionally comfortable during
their pregnancy have children less inclined to colic and less inclined to hyperactivity. The old wives tale which tells of the
child who is marked by the frightening experiences of the
mother, may yet prove to have some basis in fact. I'm sure you
are all familiar with the tuning fork experiments, in which
children are observed fluoroscopically while a tuning fork is
placed against the mother's abdomen. These children have a

---

[2] Film, *The Interaction Between Child and Environment*, Norton and Co.
1. *Some Basic Differences in New Born Infants during the Lying-in-
   Period.* New York University Film Library.

startle reflex in utero. Following their birth, however, these children do not have as marked a startle reflex as do unconditioned children. This suggests that children may be influenced by environment prior to birth. There are, of course, other congenital influences that we might discuss. I refer to such matters as the areas of implantation of the ovum in the uterine wall, the critically important matter of the sex of the child, and other factors which we need not here review. I leave these to your imagination.

Let us, however, think about the influence of what we might call acts of fate on the personality and psychological structure of the person of whom you are thinking. What were the circumstances of his conception? Were they happy and growing out of love or were they unhappy? Were the circumstances of his conception accidental or were they planned? Where on this planet was he conceived? If he were conceived in Brooklyn, just a move of a few blocks would make a great difference in his later personality construction. If he were born in Philadelphia, Iowa, New Delhi, Havana, London or Capetown, wouldn't this play a part in his personality construction? What is his ordinal position in the family? How many siblings does he have? What are their ages and of what sex are they? Surely, child psychiatry has contributed enough to our knowledge of human personality for us to believe that these matters are of great importance. What are the economic, social, and educational positions of his parents? A child born of well-to-do parents is likely to have a somewhat different view of life than a child born of poor parents. If he is born of *nouveau riche* parents, he is also likely to have a somewhat different point of view and structure of thinking than if he is born of parents accustomed to material comfort. If his parents have had the advantage of some education, won't they provide him with different opportunities for psychological stimulation than less well-educated parents? Surely the religion, which your patient acquires as an act of fate, will play a large part in his verbalizations to you. Would he not be a different type of person if only this factor were different?

Erikson (1950, 1959), discusses, at great length, the influence of the history of the child's parents and of the group to which they belong as they affect the handling, behavior and personality structure of the child. Such simple matters as the occupational activity of the child's parents, whether these occupational activities interfere with the physical care of the child or cause the parents to be absent from home for long periods of time, also influence the growing personality and structure of the child. Similarly, the health or illness of a parent, whether or not one parent is in poor health or may have died, will influence your patient. These are obvious acts of fate. There are more subtle acts of fate. What is the marital relationship between his parents? Did both parents want him? What are their attitudes toward child-rearing, feeding, and discipline? Can they do much to modify these attitudes? Should we not now look to the attitudes toward child-rearing, feeding, toilet training, and discipline shown by our patient's grandparents or perhaps even the attitudes of his great grandparents?

If we are to understand his psychology, we must know that the unconscious attitudes of his parents are as important as their conscious attitudes. We know that when a crisis arises, even when a child's parents are protected by conscious intellectual knowledge, they will lean back on their unconscious attitudes which have been, in turn, determined by the unconscious attitudes of their parents and their parents' parents. The transference reactions and fantasies of a set of parents toward their unborn child, whether these transference reactions be positive or negative, will surely influence the child's early handling and management and will carry through much of his childhood, should his parents be unable to resolve these unconscious transference attitudes. Is the unborn child seen as a loved parent or a hated parent, as a loved sibling or a hated sibling? Child psychiatrists, of course, pay some attention to the time at which the mother and father begin to call the child by his name, for we know that as long as the child is called "Baby," the object relations of his parents to him are determined by transference and not by reality. As long as a child is managed in accordance with the unconscious dreams, fantasies, and transferences of his parents, he cannot grow and develop as a person in his own right. He is unwittingly driven to act in accordance with the dreams, attitudes and transferences of his parents, just as is true of the patient whose psychiatrist or psychoanalyst, through unconscious countertransferences, anticipates infantile gratifications from his patient.

This is not to imply that the biology, heredity, instinctual structure, and even physical appearance, in a newborn child, do not play their own fateful role in contributing to the reactions and attitudes of his parents. Recent research has indicated that the parents of organically damaged children are equal in emotional instability to the parents of psychotic children. The conclusions drawn from this research suggests that it is the child's illness that causes the emotional instability in his parents and not the emotional instability of the parents that causes the illness. Some current studies suggest that the hyperactivity and unmanageability of schizophrenic children are responsible for the ambivalent attitudes and emotional disturbances of their parents, rather than the reverse. Of course, the predominant view is still that the psychology of parents contributes to the genesis of schizophrenia in children. Those of you who have had to care for the colicky child or whose patients have had colicky infants are familiar with the changes in maternal personality that follow several nights of walking the floor with the infant. Equally valid studies demonstrate beyond question, however, that parental disturbances and even parental defense mechanisms are transmitted to children and result in pathology in the child.

I have taken this time to review the many predetermined influences on the current psychology of your patient, as a re-

minder of the incredibly large number of variables that we
cannot influence in a way we would wish, but which determine
our patient's personality structure and psychology. I have not
even attempted to be comprehensive in listing or discussing
these variables with you. I have omitted such important influences as the attitudes of his obstetrician, the nature of the
delivery procedure, the place where the delivery is conducted,
the nature of the nurses who care for the mother during her
labor, and a multitude of other factors. Notice, however, that
after this long review of basic material, we have only now
arrived at a point in our fantasied patient's life where he has
begun to become amenable to outside influences and we only
now approach a place where our knowledge of child development and maturation can offer us the opportunity to study
him, to understand him, and to modify his psychology. We
must now admit that if we are to understand him, we must live
his life with him, day by day, to understand his reactions as
he grows, to think with him, to feel with him and to experience
with him. This is, of course, an impossibility. We have an opportunity to understand only one human being in our existence, in this detail, and even our understanding of this one
human being is inhibited by biology, repression, and other
factors. Most of us will agree with the authorities, who tell us
that the newborn child, except for the matters already discussed, is subject to the widest variation of influences, beginning with his first feeding and nurturing experiences. His
mind is more open than it will ever be again. Concomitantly,
it is less capable of self-direction than it will ever be again.

Until recently, we had thought that the newborn's instincts
to suck and to satisfy hunger were the controlling influences in
the first year. Now, there are hints, in recent research, that the
newborn child has additional instinctual requirements which
will play a critical part in his later psychology. We have known,
since Freud's early discovery and the later elaborations of psychoanalysts, that eating and sucking instincts must be satisfied

if the child is to survive his first year. The studies of Spitz, Levy, and others have indicated the importance of a constant mothering figure and, at least twenty years ago, Margaret Ribble (1943) was aware that marasmus and death occurred in children when outside human stimulation was inadequate or missing. The animal psychologists, now called ethologists, have given us reason to believe that there are additional instincts, beside the drive to satisfy hunger and the drive to suck, in the newborn. They have discovered that there is a critical period in the life of a newborn animal, during which it experiences what seems to be a biological process that has been termed "imprinting." In the case of geese, Hess (1957) has discovered that a newborn goose will follow any moving white object on an instinctual basis, even a piece of paper. Should the only moving white object, in the first sixteen hours in the life of a goose, be a piece of paper, that goose will henceforth react to that piece of paper as if it were its mother and behave in a neurotic way when the moving piece of paper is not available. Similarly, the goose so imprinted will not react to other fowl of its species in an adequate manner for the rest of its life. Similar studies by Harlow (1958), with monkeys, have led to the belief that primates are also subject to the imprinting process and have defects in object relationships when imprinting takes place with other than a living maternal object.

Bowlby (1960), in his paper on separation anxiety, suggests that, in addition to the instinct to suck and to satisfy hunger, the human infant has the instinct to cling, to follow, to smile, and to cry. Bowlby has further suggested that these hypothesized instinctual responses of newborn infants produce accompanying instinctual responses in parental figures, which tend to promote the object relations of the child and the mothering reactions of the parent. Thus, when a child smiles and clings to the fingers of his parent, these actions produce a pleasant emotional reaction in the father or mother which tends to bind the child closer to the parental figure. By the same token, when an infant cries, the cry provokes concern and discomfort, on the part of its parents, which Bowlby calls instinctual. Additional experimental studies with very young infants suggest that the smiling response can be produced in two months old babies by a balloon or even a mask of the human face and these studies have led Bowlby to believe imprinting takes place in human infants, as well as in other primates and lower animals. The crying, smiling, clinging, and following instincts supposedly promote imprinting. When we compare this thinking of Bowlby, Harlow, Hess, Lorenz, and others interested in ethology, with the studies of children by Spitz, Levy, Ribble and others, it suggests to us that later object relations and even body image are determined early in the first year of the life of a child. Thus, we suspect new maturational patterns which, if properly stimulated by parental figures, may produce individuals with good object relations and a comparable body image, and if inadequately stimulated, may lead to psychological illness in childhood or later life. These ethological investigations by child psychiatrists and animal psychologists only hint at the discoveries, concerning the instinctual and the maturational factors, which we have yet to make.

For the purpose of understanding later material in this paper, let us distinguish between imprinting and an instinctual drive. Imprinting is a one time, all-or-nothing process, which must take place during a biologically determined and limited period of time. This period is called the "critical period." In Hess' experiments with geese, it was the first sixteen hours of the bird's life. Once this critical period is passed in lower animals, it is gone forever and nothing can be done to change the situation. Instinctual drives, however, are repetitive, continuous, and modifiable by environment. They, too, are biological, seeming to appear at specific age periods in the maturational process. They accompany the appearance of abilities we are accustomed to call ego attributes or functions. Visual perception, for example, is called an ego function and appears in primitive form during the very early oral period. Visual perceptions are psychologically linked with the oral drive, a linkage which may contribute to such difficulties in children as an inability to read. In the area of perception alone, we have concepts of perceptual experiences which may be influenced by the very early object relationship processes which the ethologists call imprinting.

Piaget (1954), in his book on reality construction (a chapter of which paradoxically enough is entitled "The Development of Object Concept"), extensively studies children's ability to abstract the existence of tangible objects. He determined that at six months a child looks for a missing tangible object only in the place where he last saw it and is unable to abstract or develop a mental image or fantasy of the lost object. He is unable to search for it. Only three months later, at age nine months, he is readily able to follow disappearing objects with his eyes and to abstract, fantasy or guess where the missing object might be. Those of you who have had to protect your glasses from exploring six-month-old fingers, know that if you take your glasses and put them behind your back the youngster continues to explore your face and cannot imagine where the glasses have gone. Try this at nine months, however, and he will jump out of your arms and immediately look for the glasses behind your back, since he is capable of following and abstracting their existence out of his direct vision. He can see them with his mind even though he does not see them with his eyes. These experimental studies of Piaget, discussed and reviewed along with the hypotheses of Bowlby and the experiments of the ethologists, give us some new views of the varieties of perception and the consequent varieties of human object relationships that are possible, even within the first few months of a child's life. These may have far reaching influences on the later personality of the child and on our hypothetical adult patient or friend.

Let us add another variable to this already confusing array.

Let us make the supposition that a youngster is brought up in an institution, or even in his own home, under circumstances which would lead to hospitalism, marasmus that is, as the result of inadequate human contact and human stimulation. As many such children do, he succumbs to secondary infection, he develops a pyogenic disease which threatens his life. At the time of Ribble's original studies, prior to the appearance of antibiotics, it was impossible to study many of these children because they died of the secondary infection. Now, with antibiotics, the child's physical existence is salvaged, even though his psychological existence is damaged. What effect will this modification of nature's balance have on the incidence of severe emotional disturbances in children? How many more surviving children do we see now who are inadequate in their object relationships because their physical existence is salvaged through the use of antibiotics? We are not yet sufficiently experienced to say. We do know that David Levy[3] estimated, in the early 1940's, that two out of six hundred children brought to his Child Guidance Clinic were suffering from some psychoses or disturbances in ego boundaries which one might equate to adult psychoses. Thus, Levy's figures suggest an incidence of psychosis of about three-tenths of 1 per cent in the average Child Guidance Clinic. Present figures, however, in Child Guidance Clinics, suggest the incidence of psychoses to be much higher. Is this perhaps related to the salvaging of psychologically damaged children, or is it due to improved diagnostic techniques in recent years? This suggests another area of study and investigation in child development and reminds us of the longitudinal studies of children which are being carried on by Child Guidance teams throughout the country, the best known of which is being conducted at Yale.

We have talked at length about infancy, but have said little about the ego, libidinal drives, the importance of breast feed-

---

[3] Lectures to Staff of U.S.P.H.S. Hospital, Lexington, Ky.

ing versus bottle feeding, or the importance of weaning; we have made no mention of the influence of the oral period on later personality and character development. The observations, of course, of Freud, Abraham, Anna Freud, and others in these areas remain unchanged. The character traits of greed versus generosity; dependence versus independence; optimism versus pessimism; and the need to solve problems with one's mouth as opposed to other more successful techniques of solving personal problems and conflicts, are not in any way modified or influenced by these more recent discoveries. Rather, it is the theoretical base provided by the work of Freud, Abraham, and Anna Freud that enables us to view with a less-jaundiced eye the contributions of the more recent investigations.

Certainly the anxiety of the human infant, when he learns that his mother can leave him, is termed "separation anxiety" in our terminology. The works of the ethologists suggest the relationships between separation anxiety, the need for mothering as demonstrated by Spitz, and the anxiety patterns of human infants when separated from their mothers, as being comparable to the anxiety patterns of lower animals when they are separated from their mothers or the objects to which they have imprinted. At the same time, while they contribute to our understanding of hospitalism, anaclitic depression, and object relations in human children, Piaget's experimental studies of the child's perception of tangible objects help us understand why a child is so uncomfortable at six months when he knows that his mother has momentarily left him, while at nine months he is comfortable in her temporary absence. Perhaps, earlier than nine months, the child is so uncomfortable in his mother's absence, or when she leaves him, because he cannot imagine that she continues to exist elsewhere.

It becomes an even more fascinating speculation when we consider Anna Freud's observation that object constancy in the normal child is not fully established until around 3½ years, which she considers an appropriate age for the child to attend nursery school. Prior to this age, most children are in difficulty when separated from their mothers, because they have not yet been able to establish a firm, internalized or incorporated mother, who continues to exist in their world even though she is no longer physically present. Thus, in the mother's physical absence the child becomes uncomfortable and develops distortions in his reality testing as well as breaches in his ego. There are literally hundreds of thousands of children in the United States at present who suffer from this type of ego distortion. These are the institutionalized children, so many of whom suffer from what Gesell used to call "pseudosymptomatic retardation." There is very spotty and distorted reality testing in these children, who may be very adept in one area but very limited in others. These are the children who are obviously bright but do not know how to tell time, who cannot tell one season from another, who cannot tell you the sequence of months, and who are not aware of the simplest of facts, even though they are in the 7th and 8th grades. These same institutionalized children seem ultimately to recover their sensorium after many, many years of living in the real world. Does this recovery of function in these children suggest the reversibility of defects resulting from early lack of nurturing and are these comparable to defects of imprinting in animals?

How different the world looks from beneath the dining room table, beneath the chair, from the floor, and from knee-level, than it does to an adult. The separation of what is important from what is unimportant, the focus on values considered socially desirable and undesirable, are of course fired in the flame of maternal affection and mother-child object relationships. How much change goes on in the ego of a youngster from the time he weighs seven pounds at birth to the time he weighs eighteen or nineteen pounds at one year; what a vast number of impressions and characterological determinations are made during this period of time. There is a constant interchange between the child, his biology, his instincts, the world around him, his environment, and the important people around him who determine his frame of reference.

Now let us turn to another consideration. Let us assume that instincts are really constant, that they remain the same from one child to the next, that they do not vary in strength or force, that only the ways in which the world deals with these instincts are variable. Even then, the influences and modifications of these instincts by the world would be vast and limitless.

For example, picture the somewhat older child, the child from twelve to twenty-four months of age. The overwhelming influence of his oral interests are beginning to wane and he has come under the influence of his anal instincts, with the accompanying fear of loss of love and concern for strength and power. Let us assume that he was living in the wilderness, in 1850, with his family who would care much more for his physical safety than for his cleanliness. This child would, in warmer months, be allowed to roam without restrictive clothing, without concern for his toilet habits, because the wilderness was limitless. The fashioning and framing of his anal instincts would then tend to create character traits which were exuberant, unrestricted and concerned with real matters. He would be less fearful of loss of control than he would be of outside danger and would tend to externalize his aggressions to conquer the unknown around him.

Let us now move the same child to a tenement in New York City, in the 1920's. Still under the influence of the anal instinct, it would be very important to this child's parents that he control his sphincters and that he remain clean and unsoiled, because diapers are expensive and difficult to wash under tenement circumstances. We might speculate that, while the instinct and the child were the same, the resulting personality would be very much different—much more of what we might call obsessive in adults than was the case with the child who had been raised in the wilderness seventy years before. Now add only one variable, an automatic washer and dryer in the basement, and, again, the mother's view of his toilet training and bowel and bladder functions would drastically change, and, along with it, the child's morality, view of himself, body image, object relations, and ability to draw freely on his inner resources, would change.

Erikson (1950), in his publications, has discussed the influence of history, social, cultural, and anthropological patterns on the framing and modification of instincts in very considerable detail. These and other influences affect the child. In this review, we have barely touched on prebirth influences, influences during the first year of life, and the modifications of character and behavior occasioned by toilet training practices during the youngster's second year.

We have touched little, if at all, on the limited perspectives and ways of viewing the world of the individual who is dominated by primary process thinking, whose world is timeless, who thinks in symbols, who uses displacement freely, in whom negatives can exist side by side without contradiction, and whose view of the world is entirely instinctual and concrete, and only becoming less so under the influence of time and mother love. Not only are there a multitude of prebirth variables, not only are there instincts which may be handled in an ever-changing variety of ways, not only is there a world which provides an ever-changing variety of experiences, but now we must also see an ego which perceives the world as an ever-changing variety of perceptions viewed by an exceedingly primitive perceptual apparatus. A father, watching a television debate prior to the last Presidential election, said of a participant, "He will tear him to bits." The child watched the television screen patiently and in fascination. When the program was over he turned to his father and said, "Daddy, when is he going to tear him to bits?" It is this kind of thinking we observe clinically, which is more understandable and more easily dealt with than the hypothetical and theoretical influences on children that we have discussed up to now.

Let us consider the case of a child who came to a psychiatrist because of a fear of going out on the street alone. The psychiatrist spent long months of patient work with the youngster, as a result of which, the child was relieved of his phobias. The psychiatrist learned in the course of his work with the youngster that he was a happy child, with loving parents, whose mother was very close to him; that the child was especially fond of his bath and enjoyed being wrapped up in a turkish towel at the conclusion of his bath. To the child it was a turkish "Tile" and he loved it. Soon thereafter, he heard the story of Peter Pan on television and read some of the Just-So stories. As he was completing his toilet training he became afraid that he would be bitten by a crocodile and later his mother learned that she could control him if she threatened him with reptiles, which he pictured as snakes. Still later, when the new baby came along, this older child was very angry at his mother because it was a brother instead of a sister. He then began to be afraid of gentiles, which was the reason for his fear of walking out on the street. He feared a gentile stranger would take him away from his mother. Here we see, in outline, not only the influence of his instincts, genital drives, aggression, fear of castration, Oedipus complex, fear of loss of control of instinctual drives, and fear of retribution, but also the influence of his race and religion, and the attitudes of his parents. All of this is compounded by his own particular point of view, his own distortions, his own nonrecognition of the strange language of adults. We see a continuous and complicated process, which could only be touched upon in his therapy and which his mother summarized when she asked, "How do we know the therapy helped? How do we know he just didn't grow out of it?" The child's therapist had to answer, "We really don't know, we can only find out by turning back the clock and letting him live this time without his therapy."

In our review of the influences affecting an individual, we have considered heredity, instinctual drives, congenital influences, parental psychology and transference, acts of fate, the inept perceptions of the immature ego, and the distortions of the unsophisticated ego. We have also made indirect reference to the species-specific maturational phases, the oral, anal, phallic, and oedipal periods, and their contributions to the patient's psychology. We also spoke in some detail of a special type of maturational pattern which is dependent upon environmental stimulation. This maturational pattern is called imprinting, by the ethologists. It has a well known analogue in the development of the individual. There is no comparable pattern for the ethologists to study, however, for the analogue to imprinting is the development of the superego or conscience. Animals have no superego, so far as we can determine, whereas human beings do, if they are raised in a society. The nature of the superego varies from individual to individual in accordance with parental attitudes incorporated at the time of massive repression, around the age of six. This, like imprinting, seems to be a one time, all-or-none process which cannot be redone at a later date. Thus, if the patient has a defective superego, a superego which does not cause him pain at the same time as the superego of most members of society, you cannot create this for him. You can improve his reality testing. You can teach him how the rest of us feel about asocial behavior, to avoid this behavior while people are watching (just as you can teach a dog to stay out of the bedroom when you are around). You cannot teach a human being to feel internal pain at transgressions when there is no possibility of discovery if the critical period, around the age of six, has passed.

Berta Bornstein's illustration, concerning an artistic child, is an excellent example.[4] This young girl, when a preschool child, was offered every opportunity for artistic expression and

---

[4] Verbal communication.

her productions, although abstract and childish, produced great pleasure in her parents. As she passed through latency, however, her productions remained abstract, although they improved in quality. This distressed her parents, for they disliked abstract art and hoped their daughter would turn her talents to more realistic productions as she became more mature. It was too late, however, as their earlier attitudes were incorporated long ago. We may say they were imprinted, and their daughter received internal pleasure from her abstract productions which was sufficient for her to ignore her parents' complaints and nagging. The superego and ego-ideal were fixed. The critical period had passed.

We suggest, then, that the process of superego formation, the capacity to achieve internal pleasure or pain not dependent on current environment, is a species-specific imprinting process occurring only in humans prior to or coincident with latency, as an all-or-none, one time process, like imprinting in animals. So that there be no confusion regarding this, let us also state that, since humans have the capacity for interpersonal communication, an unreasonable superego can be modified by psychiatric care under certain circumstances. Since we cannot communicate with animals, except in a superficial way, we are unable to influence the imprinting process in animals.

When no superego is developed during the critical period, however, it is extremely unlikely that this structure can be formed at a later date. It is for this reason that our government has such difficulty in communicating with governments of very different cultural backgrounds—and perhaps it is the explanation of our government's failure in attempts to superimpose our superego on other governments, the results being comparable to the efforts of the parents of the young artist we discussed a few minutes ago.

Psychiatrists have demonstrated the futility of developing superegos in feral children and have thus implied that superego formation has a critical period. Similar patterns seem to apply to learning and there is apparently a critical period for learning to read and for other skills.

This discussion has not yet considered the influence of latency, the variable acts of fate which may influence our patient from birth to latency, the effects of extra-familial influences on later personality or even that most remarkable species-specific period in humans which we call adolescence, a time when we have the opportunity to re-do or fix earlier errors. We have, of course, omitted much that would properly belong in a more comprehensive synthesis.

In this discussion, I have tried to convey to you a view of the infinitely complicated nature of human personality structure, which may, in some ways, apologize for our ignorance of children, their psychology, and the nature of childhood. I hope I have also conveyed to you my own impressions of the infinitely complicated problem of preventive psychiatric work with children. Finally, I hope I have given you some stimuli for further thought.

BIBLIOGRAPHY

Bowlby, J. (1960), Separation Anxiety. *International Journal of Psychoanalysis,* XLI:89-113.

Erikson, E. (1950), *Childhood and Society.* New York: Norton & Co.

—— (1959), Identity and the Life Cycle. *Psychological Issues.*

Greenacre, P. (1952), *Trauma Growth and Personality.* New York: Norton & Co.

Harlow, H. and R. Zimmerman (1958), The Development of Affectional Responses in Infant Monkeys. *American Philosophical Society, 102*: 501-509.

Hess, E. (1957), Paper on Water Fowl—Effects of Meprobamate on Imprinting Waterfowl. *Ann. New York Acad. Science,* 724-733.

Levy, D. (1937), Primary Affect Hunger. *American Journal of Psychiatry, 94*:643-652.

Piaget, J. (1954), *The Construction of Reality in the Child,* 3-97. New York: Basic Books.

Ribble, M. (1943), *The Rights of Infants.* New York: Columbia University Press.

Spitz, R. (1947), Anaclitic Depression. *The Psychoanalytic Study of the Child,* 2:313-342. New York: International Universities Press.

Anxiety and Phobias

IRVING BIEBER, M.D.

The term "anxiety" is commonly used to mean (a) the response to threat and (b) the anxiety response combined with the anxiety-provoking stimulus. For example, one refers to "acute" and "chronic" anxiety, and one refers to anxieties about rejection, authority, sexuality, and so forth. In this latter instance, the anxiety-provoking situation is stressed. To achieve clarity of definition (which often tends to be neglected in psychiatric writing), I believe the term "anxiety" should be restricted to its biophysiological connotation.

Freud's earliest concept of anxiety was that it was a response to a danger situation. When he formulated the libido theory he then viewed anxiety as resulting from inhibited or repressed libido. According to this later construct, libidinal energy that could not be expressed directly in behavior, to fulfill gratification, was dammed up and could manifest itself in an anxiety reaction. Thus anxiety was thought to be the result of repressed libidinal energy. In 1926, Freud revised his concept of anxiety and returned to his earlier formulation. In *An Outline of Psychoanalysis,* published posthumously in 1940, the following statement is contained: "An increase in unpleasure which is expected and foreseen is met by a signal of anxiety; the occasion of this increase, whether it threatens from without or within, is called a 'danger.' " The major emphasis was on the signaling aspect of anxiety. This signal "alerted the ego" to the danger situation. Although the anxiety reaction has, or can have, a signaling effect even where danger is unconsciously perceived, in my view, the signaling effect is only one aspect of a complex biological response. For example, though pain may signal the presence of pathology, I do not conceive of pain as simply a "signal," but rather as a by-product of the involvement of nerve endings in a pathological process. I define anxiety as a biophysiological, defensive reaction to a perception of threat of injury, the perception occurring at any level of consciousness. Anxiety is a term used to describe a complex of responses that are objective manifestations of the hypermobilization of major resource systems, preparatory to meeting a situation of danger. These objective manifestations include tachycardia, transitory hypertension, hyperglycemia, increased metabolic rate, tachypnia, increased muscular tension and, in general, a sharpening of all sensibilities, including subjective feelings of distress. From a psychobiological viewpoint, the clinical picture is that of a "pepped-up" organism readying itself to meet a danger by "fight" or "flight." Anxiety is a nonspecific defensive reaction which occurs with the perception of any type of threat. The intensity of reaction reflects the estimation of the degree of danger. In turn, the estimation of danger represents an equating of the nature of the threat and the perceived capacity to master it.

Although much is known about the highly complex physiology of the acute anxiety reaction, certainly, a great deal more remains to be discovered. Selye demonstrated that this reaction does not take place in adrenolectomized animals, indicating that adrenal participation in the acute anxiety reaction is essential. Udenfriend and his co-workers have shown that the enzyme for the synthesis of norepinephrine in the adrenal medulla also exists in equal concentration in the caudate nucleus. Although actual secretion of norepinephrine has not been demonstrated in the caudate nucleus, the existence of an enzyme for the production of norepinephrine is strongly suggestive. One may speculate that such a secretion takes place with acute anxiety and that the biophysiological defensive reaction of acute anxiety is so critical for the survival of the organism, that the brain itself is equipped to secrete hypermobilizing substances. The experimental work of Morris B. Bender, about twenty years ago, involved the relationship of acetylcholine to the fright reaction. Bender observed the response of the Macacus Rhesus monkeys to the threat-attack gestures he made with a hose. He called the animals' behavioral response "the fright reaction"; Selye would call such a response "the alarm reaction"; I refer to it as "an acute anxiety reaction." In the course of his work, Bender sectioned the facial nerve and permitted it to degenerate. After ten days, the degenerated muscle became exquisitely sensitive to minute doses of acetylcholine intravenously injected. He noted that when the monkeys were threatened and the acute anxiety reaction ensued, the denervated muscle went into the same type of fibrillation as when acetylcholine was intravenously injected— thus suggesting a secretion of acetylcholine or an acetylcholine-like substance during an acute anxiety reaction. It would be fruitful to replicate Bender's early work, in order to determine whether a secretion of acetylcholine or an acetylcholine-like substance occurs in adrenolectomized animals.

As already indicated, the acute anxiety reaction is a nonspecific defensive reaction to any perception of threat or danger. The threat can be that of physical injury, rejection, material loss, and so forth—in short, any danger of injury to the self. Any stimulus perceived to be detrimental to an optimal state, at any particular moment in personal history, may be defined as a potential injury. One's perception of injury and concept of an optimal state may exist at any level of psychosomatic integration and may or may not be capable of conscious formulation. The individual may perceive injury or threat accurately or he may perceive threat when it does not exist. The anxiety reaction is an automatic response to the perception of threat, whether or not the individual is accurately perceiving reality. As emphasized earlier, anxiety is a biophysiological reaction; in itself, it is nonpathological. The basis for pathology is the erroneous perception of threat as a consequence of an erroneous belief.

Erroneous beliefs are, in the main, either the consequences of realistic injury in the past experience, projected transferentially to a current situation, or the result of erroneous interpretations of past events. An example of an erroneous belief resulting from past injury would be an individual who, having been brought up in a repressive environment, still believes, as an adult, that all people in positions of authority are repressive. Such an individual may expect all authority figures to be repressive. He will be unusually alert to repressive cues and will selectively concentrate attention on those authority figures who, in fact, are repressive. Though his perceptions may be accurate, his selectivity distorts the total reality since nonauthoritarian leaders are excluded from his frame of reference. Hence, his original conviction that all authority figures are repressive is continually reinforced. Selectivity, followed by reinforcement of erroneous beliefs, plays an important role in maintaining the chronicity of psychopathology. An example of an erroneous belief arising from misinterpretation of reality was brought to my attention in the case of a child who had burned his fingers on an electric heater and consequently became afraid to touch anything colored red. A more common illustration is that of a nonpreferred child who believes that his excelling over a preferred child will displace the rival in parental affections. When such a belief is maintained in adult life, it usually results in destructive and pathological competitiveness.

To re-emphasize the point made above, the anxiety reaction is not pathological. It is imprecise to refer to "appropriate" anxiety, "normal" anxiety or "realistic" anxiety, and then to contrast these terms with "neurotic" anxiety. Anxiety itself is appropriate. It is, rather, the inaccurate perception of threat that is inappropriate or "neurotic."

Thus far, I have directed my remarks to the "acute" types of anxiety reactions. I would like to comment upon so-called "chronic tension states" or "chronic anxiety." These may be defined as states of chronic hyperdefensiveness. Individuals in chronic tension states may be compared to armies or nations in a constant state of alert against an anticipation of imminent attack. Clinical manifestations of such states may include a general hyper-alertness involving all sensory modalities, increased muscle tone, and tension expressed in excessive motor response to sudden stimuli, such as hyperreflexia. The physiology of chronic anxiety and tension is not well understood, although some of the elements involved may be similar to those operative in acute anxiety reactions. It is not likely that these tension states represent merely watered-down versions of acute anxiety. Selye (1956) states, "The symptom of all those non-specific systemic reactions of the body which ensue upon long, continued exposure to stress has been termed 'the general adaptation syndrome.' It is characterized by a number of morphological and functional changes. Among the most prominent of these are: enlargement of the adrenal cortex with increased corticoid hormone secretion; involution of the thymus and other lymphatic organs, gastro-intestinal ulcers, certain metabolic changes, and variations in the resistance of the organism." The relationship of pathophysiological manifestations in chronic tension states to Selye's general adaptation syndrome remains to be determined. There is, however, clinical evidence that certain disease entities, such as hypertension, hyperthyroidism, gastric ulcers, and ulcerative colitis, have some relationship to chronic tension and chronic anxiety states. I suspect that the pathophysiology and biochemical changes reported in schizophrenics are also the consequences of chronic, biological defensive reactions. I wish to emphasize that chronic tension states or chronic anxiety states are responses to more or less continuous perceptions of threat of injury. In this sense, such states are similar to the acute reactions which are also responses to perceptions of injury.

A differentiation must be made between defenses against anxiety and defenses against the threatening situations creating the anxiety. An individual who shoots a threatening lion, or runs away from it, does not do so merely to defend himself against anxiety; he is defending himself against destruction. Many of the defenses we are accustomed to think of as defenses against anxiety are, in fact, defenses against the threatening situations which set off anxiety responses. Although the anxiety reaction itself is basically a biophysiological reaction necessary for self-preservation (and that of the species), it also has potentially destructive effects requiring defenses against it. A severe anxiety state of lengthy duration constitutes a severe drain on the physiological resources of the individual. Before shock treatment was used, I saw patients in acute states of mania who died as a result of what seemed to be a "burning-out" of themselves. Severe anxiety interferes with normal thinking, probably because of its interference with normally integrated cerebral functioning. We are all aware of the defective judgment and behavior often accompanying severe anxiety in panic states. Subjective feelings accompanying anxiety states are uncomfortable and distressing. Individuals show varying degrees of tolerance for these painful affects.

Defenses against anxiety may be categorized as follows:

1. *Physiological Defenses.* I offer the hypothesis that there is

a built-in mechanism for inhibiting the anxiety reaction after it has gone on for some time. This hypothesis is based on observations made while watching individuals during acute anxiety reactions to a reality threat, such as a serious illness of a loved one. I noticed that there tended to be fluctuations in the manifestations of the anxiety. The individuals concerned would appear to be acutely anxious for a period of time and then for no apparent reason, since the reality threat remained unaltered, they tended to quiet down for a period of time, only to become intensely anxious again. There may be mechanisms that come into play that cause the tissues to become refractory to the substances involved in the anxiety reaction. It would appear that an as-yet-unknown physiological mechanism is operative in maintaining a metabolic homeostasis. Sleep is a common physiological mechanism for restoring homeostasis, in that noxious stimuli can be shut out. Many individuals go to sleep when they are feeling anxious. Those who can sleep when anxious shut out those perceptions of threatening stimuli which are triggering the anxiety reactions. As physicians, we utilize the protective sleep mechanism by means of narcotic therapy, to be discussed later.

In children, a series of mechanisms appear to be related to controlling the anxiety reaction. Sucking is one such mechanism. When a child is disturbed or anxious, his own thumbsucking, or a pacifier, will tend to calm him. In general, several of the mechanisms classified by Freud under "narcissism," such as sucking and infantile masturbation, appear to have the capacity of shutting out distressing external stimuli. In adults, such mechanisms have their counterpart in eating, smoking or drinking excessively, during anxiety states. Some individuals seek respite from anxiety in sexual activity. Strenuous motor activity is another mechanism which appears to reduce anxiety reactions. Behavior such as crying, vomiting, or diarrhea, which may occur during an acute anxiety reaction, has the effect of lowering the intensity of anxiety. There appears to be a series of physiological mechanisms at the service of the organism for ameliorating acute anxiety reactions.

2. *Pharmacological Defenses.* In most cultures, no matter how primitive, a drug (or drugs) to diminish anxiety has been discovered. Such drugs are either alcohol or alkaloids. When taken in large doses, these drugs disturb consciousness and shut out an awareness of threatening stimuli. Even when taken in moderate doses, the drugs are generally quite effective. Apart from the "shut-out" mechanism, the drugs probably act on elements involved in the biochemistry of the anxiety reaction. The variety of drugs which have come into psychiatric use, in the past thirty years, act upon some aspect of the anxiety reaction. Inasmuch as drugs do not alter belief systems supporting erroneous convictions leading to inappropriate responses, it is only the physiological aspects of anxiety which are affected by the use of drugs. Most drugs, after a while, lose their effectiveness or require increasing dosages.

3. *Psychological Defenses.* Psychological defenses against anxiety include mechanisms which distort and deny the existence of threatening impulses. An individual may so distort a threatening situation that it will appear as a friendly and helpful situation to him. I recall a schizophrenic soldier who was a member of an antiaircraft battalion. He had been subjected to a considerable amount of aerial bombardment, yet he described the experience as "pleasant" to him, since his superior officer would appear after each bombardment to ask how he felt. In this case, the major orientation was to the idea of the solicitous officer. There was a complete "shut-out" of the danger implicit in a bombardment. Threat denial is obvious in those situations where apparent illness is denied. This is frequently noted in cases of malignancy.

The mechanism of *avoidance* is a psychological defense to circumvent threatening stimuli which evoke the anxiety reaction. In some individuals, avoidance is the dominant reactive tendency toward anxiety-provoking situations and activities.

For example, a person who develops anxiety when faced with the possibility of sexual activity may avoid any potentially sexual situation. Avoidance mechanisms lead to personality constriction and preclude the resolution of problems underlying anxiety responses.

Displacement is a type of avoidance mechanism. An anxiety-provoking stimulus is symbolically displaced to an object which is then avoided. The phobias exemplify this type of displacement mechanism.

Phobias arise from an impulse to an action believed to lead to injury. In the development of the phobia, three impulse types are particularly involved:

When the expression of *sexual impulses* is thought to be dangerous, as it usually is in childhood in our culture, the arousal of sexual impulses will evoke anxiety, unless defenses have been organized against its perception or expression. This especially applies to masturbatory and incestuous impulses, but may involve sexual impulses toward other objects. Phobias frequently make their appearance when the Oedipus complex is developing in childhood.

Hostile impulses include destructive impulses, such as murder, at both the perceptive and action levels. Murderous impulses in childhood are usually related to the ipso-sexual parent (Oedipus complex) and to siblings in the sibling rivalry situation.

The third impulse type is self-destructive or masochistic impulses. In a paper entitled "The Meaning of Masochism," I defined masochism as the inflicting of self-injury as a defense to avoid sustaining a greater injury. Psychotics occasionally attempt self-castration to avoid the unrealistic expectation of being murdered. In masochism, this "greater injury" is perceived on an unrealistic basis, since there is, in reality, no danger of injury whereas the self-inflicted masochistic injuries *are* destructive to self. Any situation or impulse which threatens the individual with injury, evokes anxiety and/or defensive reactions. Masochistic impulses, too, evoke anxiety and may be defended against by phobias.

Many objects can be involved in phobic displacement. Animals are common phobic objects. There are associative symbolic connections between the threatening impulse and the phobic object. In phobias (i.e., cockroach, mouse, and so forth), the color and nature of the movement are significant. Patients frequently associate the color to feces and dirt. Further associations usually establish connections to sexual and hostile impulses. The character of the movement is associated with suddenly appearing, startling, uncontrollable impulses. Not uncommonly, a slip of the tongue for the word "insect" is "incest." The cockroach, in reality, is not a dangerous animal, though many animal phobias do involve animals who are potentially dangerous, such as snakes. In such instances, the phobic component of the anxiety response to these stimuli can be concealed and rationalized. The phobic individual, however, will have almost the same degree of aversion to a replica of the object as to the object itself. Thus, a person with a mouse phobia will react negatively to a toy mouse.

The size of the object may represent a significant symbolic association to a threatening impulse. When horses were more commonly seen about town, they were frequently phobic objects. Freud's (1909) classic essay on *Little Hans* concerned a horse phobia. The size of the object may be connected with the feeling of the power of the impulse. Children, in particular, relate themselves to the large mouth and teeth of large animals. In 1935, puppet shows were presented at Bellevue Psychiatric Hospital to children for diagnostic, therapeutic and research purposes. Most children reacted with severe anxiety to the large mouth of the crocodile. Phobias which are related to the mouths of animals are usually a displacement of hostile impulses.

Phobias such as claustrophobia, agoraphobia, and acrophobia may be subsumed under the term "space phobias," since they are organized around the space factor. In claustrophobia, confined space interferes with the defense of flight and, in this sense, claustrophobia may be considered a secondary mechanism. In agoraphobia, confined space becomes a defense against threats such as the unfamiliar, the unpredictable, and the unmastered. Acrophobia is a somewhat different problem, though also related to space integration. The fear of height is, in fact, related to a built-in, ocular-vestibular mechanism. A simple example would be the protection against an animals' visualizing the drop below afforded by the use of covered bridges. The innate ocular-vestibular, neurophysiological mechanism is the substratum around which psychopathologic impulses may be organized. In acrophobia, the mechanism is integrated with psychopathologic impulses such as the masochistic impulse to jump or the sexually determined impulse to fly through space.

Although a phobia may at first be organized as a defense against a single impulse, e.g., a sexual impulse, it becomes associated with other impulses such as hostile or masochistic impulses. This is in accord with a general psychodynamic principle: there is a tendency toward economy in the organization of defenses. Thus, a phobic object, such as a mouse, may predominantly reflect anxiety about sexual impulses at one moment and, at another, may be symbolic of hostile feelings. Hence, the mechanical equation of a phobic object with a single impulse or individual (such as a sibling) is an oversimplification which does not take into account the overdetermination of symptoms in adults.

Summary: Anxiety is a biophysiological response to a perception of any type of threat. The term "anxiety" is restricted to the response and is not used to describe the threat. Thus, the term "threat of rejection" is substituted for "rejection anxiety." The latter term is viewed as imprecise. I have emphasized that anxiety, in itself, is nonpathological. Unrealistic perceptions of threat or misconceptions of danger set off anxiety responses. The items of psychopathology are the misperceptions and misconceptions, rather than the anxiety response. Acute anxiety, if excessive in intensity or duration, disturbs total organismic functioning and the functioning of important organs such as the brain, heart, and adrenals. The biophysiological defenses against excessive anxiety are differentiated from the defenses against threatening stimuli. Psychological mechanisms of defense can be organized to defend against the anxiety response, the threatening stimuli, or both.

Phobias are psychological defenses against both the anxiety response and the threatening stimuli. Phobias are symbolic expressions of threatening inner impulses displaced to external objects which are then avoided.

BIBLIOGRAPHY

Freud, S. (1909), Analysis of a Phobia in a Five-Year-Old Boy. *Collected Papers, 3*:149. London: Hogarth Press, 1950.
Selye, H. (1956), *Stress of Life*. New York: McGraw-Hill.

The Psychopathology and
Management of Paranoid States

WILLIAM G. NIEDERLAND, M.D.

The very concept of paranoia and related disorders, their position as a nosological entity, clinical classification, nomenclature, etc., have had a long, controversial, and, at times, even stormy history in our science. Since, in the official current classification of psychiatric conditions, paranoid states are listed as distinct clinical entities, I propose to deal with them within the framework of the official and, in my view, valid classification, thus avoiding the confusing multitude of nosological problems and semantic considerations, with their frequent grouping, subgrouping, and regrouping into "paranoid personalities," "paranoid trends," "paranoid reactions," "paranoid schizophrenia," and so on. The one major contribution to our knowledge of these conditions was written half a century ago by Freud (1911) and has become what may be called the analytic textbook on such diseases. Freud's monograph has also made Schreber himself "the most frequently quoted patient in psychiatry," to use MacAlpine's and Hunter's engaging formulation, (1955).

Freud, primarily interested in the patient's libidinal striv-ings and vicissitudes, focused his attention on Schreber's delu-sional system *in toto,* as it were. From the patient's grandiose belief that he had a mission to redeem the world and restore mankind to its lost state of bliss through his personal transfor-mation into a woman and his subsequent sexual union with God—a union from which a new and better race of men would then emerge—Freud extracted the delusionally distorted deriv-atives of the patient's unresolved infantile ties to his father. The latter, transformed into the superior figure of God, was recognized as the unconscious homosexual love object which, through denial and projection, undergoes the characteristic change from the unconsciously desired to the consciously dreaded, as well as hated, object, the persecutor, according to the familiar formula: "I do not love the man; I hate him; be-cause he persecutes me." Freud developed the major variants and vicissitudes of this fantasy culminating in the patient's emasculation and redemption ideas, the delusions of grandeur and persecution, and the defensive aspects of the paranoid symptoms, with projection as the mechanism characteristic of paranoia, etc.

Relatively little attention was given by Freud to the great number, peculiar quality, and elaborate description by the patient of other delusional features in his complex system, to the bizarre as well as massive type of certain physical tortures inflicted on him during his illness, such as the maltreatment of his body by God through tying and fastening by mechanical means, the compression of his head and chest by various "divine miracles," the perforation and strange "plurality" of his skull, the frequent attacks on his capacity to sit, stand, or walk, and multiple other tormenting experiences. All this the patient attributes to God's relentless actions on his body. At one point, Schreber exclaims, "If only my eyes, my kneecap, my skull, were not miracled about!"

In another passage he reports: "From the beginnings of my

contact with God up to the present time my body has been the object of divine miracles. I could fill a whole book with them alone. I may say that hardly a single limb or organ in my body escaped being damaged by miracles nor a muscle being pulled by them . . . either moving or paralyzing it according to its respective purpose. . . ."

Many more statements of this order can be found in Schreber's (1903) *Memoirs of a Neurotic,* and it was precisely the frequency, as well as the specific and graphic wording of such descriptions, which led me to investigate the possibility that "a kernel of historical truth" might be contained in the paranoid productions. Interestingly enough, Freud himself (who, in one of his last papers made this point, stating that a delusion "owes its convincing power to the element of historic truth which it inserts in the place of rejected reality") omitted the linking of this proposition to the Schreber case. It is well to remember, in this connection, that, until quite recently, Schreber, from a dynamic point of view, had been like a man without a childhood, a patient without a past, and that Freud had deliberately based his analysis on the productions of the adult patient only. It was but a few years ago that, through Baumeyer's accidental discovery (1956) of the old medical records concerning Schreber's many years of hospitalization in mental institutions, and through my own methodical research into Schreber's childhood and antecedents (1959), a notable number of heretofore obscure features and unintelligible details of Schreber's delusional system became dynamically and genetically comprehensible.

A closer examination of Schreber's bodily delusions is, indeed, rewarding. For brevity I give you only a few examples as to the origin and nature of these phenomena. Schreber, for instance, tells us, "One of the most horrifying miracles was the . . . compression-of-the-chest miracle. It consisted in my chest wall being so compressed that the oppression caused by the lack of breath affected my whole body. . . . Next to it, the most abominable of all miracles was the head-compressing-machine which compressed my head as though in a vise. . . . It was accompanied by great pain . . . and produced in the skull a deep cleft or rent roughly along the middle. . . . The compressed state usually continued for some time. . . ." Often his skull was squeezed, thinned, perforated, and sawn apart. For a time he had several heads, "a plurality of heads"—*"eine Mehrkoepfigkeit"* as he puts it—consisting of "several individuals in one and the same skull." At other times, he had to live without a stomach or gullet and with a worm in his lungs (*ein Lungewurm* at work inside his chest). His coccyx bone, his knees, and other parts of his skeleton were so damaged by divine miracles that his ability to move about was seriously interfered with.

As already stated, little was known about Schreber's childhood until very recently. (It is one of the ironies of analytic research that perhaps the most thoroughly reported and most frequently discussed psychiatric case history contained virtually no data about the patient's early life and developmental years.) Though my material is far from complete, a detailed study of the prime sources collected and investigated by me, especially the writing of the patient's father and other Schreber memorabilia (notes, letters, family documents, etc.), which I now have in my possession, has convinced me that there is a realistic core to much of this delusional material. Enormously preoccupied with his children's postural system and musculoskeletal growth, Dr. Daniel Gottlieb Meritz Schreber, the patient's father, a prominent orthopedist and medical reformer, invented a whole series of orthopedic braces and fastening devices, the so-called *Schrebersche Geradehalter,* to secure a straight, upright posture day and night. One of these contraptions consisted of iron bars arranged in such a fashion that the horizontal bar came to press against the chest of the sitting child, whenever the child tried to move into a more relaxed or at least less-rigid position than the one permitted

by the father. Another device was used at night to make sure
that the child remained in a supine position while asleep.
Belts running across the child's chest, shoulders, and legs kept
its posture supine, as well as straight, through the night. It appears likely that these unmistakably sadistic methods of mechanical coercion, enforced by the father with a peculiar mix-
ture of *unnachsichtlicher Strenge* (absolute strictness) and pa-
ternal seductiveness, not only became the nucleus of the son's
delusional "compression-of-the-chest-miracle," but also placed
it among the most horrifying ones recorded by the patient as
present reality during his illness half a century later.

To ensure the proper development of the skull, chin and
jaws, the father constructed a helmet-like *Kopfhalter* which
had to be worn by the young child for some time every day.
It is difficult to avoid the conclusion that this remarkable piece
of orthopedic machinery is the historical and realistic precur-
sor of what, in the patient's delusional system, later emerged
as the mysterious "Head-Compression-Machine." It is worth
noting that in connection with the "Head-Compression-Machine," the patient complains about a feeling as if his head was
changing its shape, the pressure on it causing pain, a cleft
along the middle, and a sensation as though his whole skull
were "in a vise" and tied together by buckled leather belts. In
other words, we have here an almost word-by-word description
of the actual experiences of the young Schreber and a striking
demonstration of the fact, stressed by Freud, that the psychotic,
like the neurotic, suffers from "reminiscences." One must best
read about these "divine miracles" in the German original
where the apparatus in question is named by the patient *das
Kopfsusammen-schnuerungswunder*, i.e., the tying-the-head-
together-miracle, a term that vividly portrays the fact of having
the head tied together with a belt or rope. In order to arrive at
the meaning of the word, which is almost as formidable as the
thing itself, one has only to drop from it the delusional "mira-

cle," the remaining word combination revealing the actual, starkly realistic core of the delusion.

What does the material just presented add up to? Although the weight to be assigned to such data for the development of the persecutory paranoid illness may be, as usual, variously appraised, it seems permissible to point to a number of factors which appear to be of practical and theoretical interest to the psychiatrist in his work with paranoid patients.

The first point I would like to make, refers to the old rule-of-thumb principle which states that "the patient is always right," or, to quote from Cameron (1959), "Many things complained of by a paranoid patient merit complaint, and sometimes fantastic things have actually happened." To reiterate this simple adage here may appear superfluous; but being mindful of it helps the psychiatrist to maintain that detached, noncommittal, yet interested attitude so necessary for his work with paranoid individuals, in whose verbose productions facts and fantasies become readily intertwined.

The second point to be extrapolated from the evidence here assembled concerns the paranoid symptomatology as such. A paranoid idea or symptom may stand, among other things, for a memory trace of a real affective experience. In this respect, the paranoid symptom resembles the hysterical one, though in the former, the mechanisms of denial and projection are chiefly involved, whereas in the latter, it is the mechanism of repression. Another difference lies in the fact that in paranoid conditions the affective experiences seem to be related to early conflicts concerning the parent of the same sex; in hysteria, it is concerned with the parent of the opposite sex.

My next point refers to the wide range and protean quality of the many obscure manifestations in Schreber's illness. This has always been a difficult question, which has given rise to numerous speculations, such as MacAlpine's and Hunter's "asexual procreation fantasies"—whatever that may be—and other daring conjectural assumptions. (MacAlpine and Hunter even go so far as to explain most of Schreber's "divine miracles" as expressions of his pregnancy and birth fantasies; for instance, regarding his report of the deep cleft in his head as an allusion to the fontanel, the compression of his skull as a reference to birth, and the like.) We now know something about the origin and nature of those protean manifestations of Schreber's illness. Through our investigation of the "divine miracles" enacted on the patient's body, it has been possible to trace those hitherto unintelligible phenomena to their traumatic origin in the early father-son relation and to correlate them with relevant experiences, of a passive, receptive, masochistic type, in his childhood. Indeed, most of the "miracles" can now be recognized as derivatives of those reactivated, archaically distorted, later "deified" experiences to which the patient was subjected by his autocratic, "omnipotent," and undoubtedly sadistic physician-father (whose middle name, incidentally, was Gottlieb) in childhood. The analytic evaluation of these protean delusional formations and their relation to certain traumatic events in the patient's childhood suggests that many of them are not only derived, almost rectilinearly, from the specific type of childhood experience, but also represents attempts at continuation and reactivation of the unresolved infantile relationship with the father; that is, he attempts to arrive, via the so-called "miracles," at psychotic object restitution.

To turn from the special pathology found in the Schreber case to paranoid states in general, let me first say that I do not believe that in every case of paranoid disorder extreme experiences of the kind discussed are present or anticipated. (Nor does every paranoiac develop the delusional idea of cohabiting with God, etc.) I do believe, however, that the essential findings of Freud's Schreber analysis are as valid today as they were half a century ago. Few, in fact, question the validity of his basic interpretative formulations. Among those who do, I already mentioned MacAlpine and Hunter. Before going into certain aspects of this controversy, I shall briefly discuss those addenda to the original interpretation which have thrown further light on paranoid development and symptomatology.

You may recall that Freud himself, after having formulated the structural hypothesis of the personality organization in *The Ego and the Id,* in 1923, re-examined the transformation of love into hate and vice versa, stressing the aggression and intense hostility engendered in the young child's restitution phenomena; that is, the patients' regressive reliving of his inverted oedipal relationship with his father.

Waelder (1951) described paranoid ideas as the result of unsuccessful denial, whereby what is denied—in this case, the passive homosexual cravings—returns in a distorted and projected fashion via fantasies and delusional formations. The significance of denial is, of course, implied in the original proposition by Freud, but has, perhaps, at times been lost sight of by overemphasizing the mechanism of projection as the main defense (against the passive homosexual wish) in paranoid states. In reality, both denial and projection are operative, as can be seen by scrutinizing the dynamic process more closely, in slow motion, so to speak. "I love him" becomes, through denial and contradiction: "I do not love him"; "I hate him"; then, through the mechanism of projection, "He hates me"; and finally, "He persecutes me."

The fact that the individual, in paranoid thinking, does not recognize his own libidinal and hostile impulses, is based on two mechanisms mainly: Denial makes for the nonrecognition and projection makes for the experience of feeling these impulses as being directed against oneself.

Finally, Kanzer (1952) and Fairbairn (1956) referred to the primal scene as a pathogenic factor in paranoid conditions. Fairbairn speaks of "the horror of the primal scene," which, according to him, is "more basic than the horror of incest," and he also points to "the utmost resistance" encountered in psychoanalytic practice, when it comes to revival of the primal scene, whether acutally witnessed or only inferred during childhood. In my experience, this holds true, especially in paranoid patients from whom we ordinarily cannot get direct evidence pertaining to primal events. In my recent study on infantile auditory experiences and the primal scene, I described individuals, most of them quite sick, who had introjected the primal scene which they had witnessed in childhood and which they "released" in analysis as intensely felt experiences of fantastic, at times almost cataclysmic, proportions. (I borrow the term "release" from Dr. Bychowski's graphic formulations on the ego and the introject.) The Schreber Memoirs seem to contain, among other things, numerous allusions to the primal scene (such as frequent references to noises, copulating, mating, etc.), to the doer and the one it is done to, and to his given names Daniel Paul—the first shared by him with his father and the second with his mother, whose name was Pauline—which may have lent themselves to concretize and reinforce such fantasies.

With this, we are back full circle to where we started out: Schreber and his early childhood. What remains is a brief examination of the criticism of those who doubt the validity of Freud's basic interpretations of paranoid dynamics and a short discussion of the treatment.

As to the criticism, I have already mentioned MacAlpine and Hunter who, though deserving full credit as excellent translators of the Schreber book, have had a less felicitous career as interpreters. Let me illustrate this (in addition to what I said about the fontanel conjecture) with an example taken from their book, *Schizophrenia 1677* (1956), in which they deal with the case of demoniacal possession described by Freud in 1923. As in their comment on Freud's Schreber analysis, they here also reject the homosexual component, asserting that there is "no shred of evidence of homosexuality" and "no trace of male genitals" in the paintings in question.

(The case of demoniacal possession concerned a sick artist, who painted his experiences with the devil in a series of pictures which were analyzed by Freud.)

A look at some of the pictures of the devil, published in the very book by MacAlpine and Hunter that contains the statement that none of the patient's paintings shows male genitalia and that therefore no homosexuality exists, would seem to controvert their position.

Of greater interest are the objections of those psychiatrists who doubt the relationship between paranoia and homosexuality as postulated by Freud. Apart from the fact that in a recent study of this problem by two descriptive psychiatrists, Klaf and Davis (1960), this relationship receives strong verification, I believe that most of the objections are due to a misunderstanding of conscious and unconscious homosexuality. In paranoid states, the homosexuality based on a passive, feminine wish is unconscious, even paradoxically, in cases of overt homosexuality.

Let me give you two clinical illustrations from my own experience. During the war, I treated a homosexual soldier who overtly engaged in anal intercourse and other homosexual practices and finally broke down with a severe paranoid psychosis—to all appearances, a clear-cut case running counter to our analytic view of paranoia. On examination, however, it turned out that to the patient his overt homosexual activities were not homosexuality at all, but a money-making device. He allowed others to perform anal penetration on him for money and, consciously, that was all there was to it, as he put it. In other words, the homosexual factor remained unconscious and completely repressed.

My second observation of this kind refers to a homosexual woman who, for years, lived in a close lesbian relationship with her girl friend, sharing room, bed, and sexual intimacies (genital sucking, mutual masturbation, etc.) with her, but who became furious at me when, in analysis, I referred to this behavior as homosexuality. She vehemently denied that she was homosexual. Her sleeping and masturbating with another woman was just an expression of her loneliness, she maintained, of her need for closeness to someone, and nothing else, least of all homosexuality, as the analyst had so crudely suggested.

Regarding treatment, a schematic presentation may perhaps serve us best. I divide the principles of treatment into two main divisions (I am omitting here the treatment of the hospitalized patient, chemotherapy, etc., since as an analyst, I rarely make use of them), as follows:

A. General Principles:
  1. Reduction of anxiety in the patient, including "Milieu Therapy."
  2. Establishment of genuine communication and confidence.
  3. Reduction of anxiety in the therapist (2nd doctor, no formal supervision, but full exchange of ideas and impressions).
B. Specific Principles, especially applicable in analysis or analytically oriented psychotherapy:
  1. Factor of suspiciousness should be approached and ventilated from the first session of analysis; the transference and the patient's transference reactions should be elicited early.
  2. Focus on feelings and experiences regarding the patient's reactions to the treatment.
  3. Focus special attention on the paranoid anxiety with regard to the treatment (e.g., artistic creativity and fears of ruining it).
  4. Focus on the immediate defenses against analysis.
  5. For a long time, no interpretation of the delusional or near-delusional productions which should be dealt with with noncommittal interested, neutral receptivity.

6. Analysis of early traumata, childhood and adolescent vicissitudes, etc.
7. Analysis of the oedipal constellation, especially retracing its inverted course.

BIBLIOGRAPHY

Baumeyer, F. (1956), The Schreber Case. *Int. J. Psy.*, XXXVII.

Cameron (1959), Paranoid Conditions and Paranoia. *American Handbook of Psychiatry*. New York: Basic Books.

Fairbairn, R. D. (1956), Considerations Arising Out of the Schreber Case. *The Brit. Journal of Medical Psychology*, XXIX: Part 2, 113-127.

Freud, S. (1911), Psychoanalytic Notes upon an Autobiographical Account of a Case of Paranoia (Dementia Paranoides). *Collected Papers, III*. London: Hogarth Press, 1948.

—— (1923), *The Ego and the Id*. London: Hogarth Press, page 77.

Kanzer, M. (1952), Manic Depressive Psychoses with Paranoid Trends. *Int. J. Psy.*, *33*: Part I, 34.

Klaf and Davis (1960), *American Journal of Psychiatry* (A Survey of 150 Cases), June.

MacAlpine, I. and R. A. Hunter (1955), *Schreber—Memoirs of My Nervous Illness*. Cambridge: Robert Bentley.

—— (1956), *Schizophrenia 1677. A Psychiatric Study of an Illustrated Record of Demoniacal Possession*. London: William Dawson & Sons, 197.

Niederland, W. G. (1959), Schreber: Father and Son. *Psy. Quart.*, XXVIII.

Schreber, D. P. (1903), *Denkwurdigkeiten eines Nervenkranken*. Leipzig: Oswald Mutze.

Waelder, R. (1951), The Structure of Paranoid Ideas. *Int. J. Psy.*, XXXII.

Obsessional Neurosis

LUDWIG EIDELBERG, M.D.

In a dream, as the result of what Freud called the dream work, an enormous amount of material is condensed into a few words. A skillful analyst, i.e., a training analyst, with the help of his students, could easily convert these few lines into a book. This would be the reverse of making a long story short. I do not have the ability to condense the whole complex problem of the obsessional neurosis into one chapter. I will therefore concentrate on only one aspect of the obsessional neurosis, namely, its structure. During this discussion I shall point out some contradictions, some weaknesses, and some things we know little or nothing about. In other words, instead of being surprised by criticisms in subsequent discussion and collapsing because of narcissistic mortification, I already anxiously anticipate such criticism.

Those of you who did not read my book, *Take Off Your Mask* (1960), will be less bored with this chapter. Those who did, might be bored, since I will refer to a case which I presented there. I will here use only a brief portion of the case, in order to present material with the help of which I shall describe the structure of the obsessional neurosis.

The patient whom I described in my book was a man who was afraid that he had little pieces of glass in his fingers. At once, perhaps, some would like to interrupt me and say, "This is not an obsessional neurosis, this is a phobia because he was afraid." Yes, that's right. I should have worded it differently. I should have said he was afraid that he may have pieces of glass in his fingers. There appears to be such little difference in the phrasing, but after some years of analyzing, just such a little detail differentiates between an obsessional neurosis and a phobia. This man was afraid that he might have little pieces of glass in his fingers and therefore had to have somebody nearby who was partly his master and partly his slave— his sister—to reassure him. She was supposed to look at his fingers and say, "No, it is all right." After a few minutes the whole thing had to be repeated. Here, you have a simple and clear example of an obsessional symptom, the obsession being that he had to ask his sister whether there was or whether there was not glass in his fingers. When he asked this question and the answer was a denial he felt relieved. If he did not ask the question, the suffering became worse. The question is typical for obsessional neuroses and represents persistent doubting.

I shall say a few words about the conscious complaints of neurotics. In the phobia, the patient says, "I will be run over by a bus." In the obsessional neurosis, he says, "I may, I don't know." In *An Outline of a Comparative Pathology of the Neuroses* (1954), I cited another patient who doubted whether or not he had syphilis. I saw him when he was still a young man and I asked, "How is the Wassermann?" He said, "Don't mention this. Obviously I can't have a Wassermann taken because it would make me very nervous." I could have said, "Wouldn't it be better to have an end to terror than terror without an end?" Such is the nature of an obsessional neurosis. It is difficult to believe that this kind of suffering represents gratification for the patient.

I said "gratification," I did not say pleasure. According to

Freud, there are two basic aims which we are all trying to achieve: avoidance of unpleasure and gain of pleasure. Originally, Freud (1910) had the idea that "whenever we avoid unpleasure, this avoidance represents the gain of pleasure." Life would be very sad if that were the case. Certainly I may avoid unpleasure. I may eliminate pleasure for instance by eating bad tasting food and experiencing no pleasure whatsoever. Pleasure is something which I may have in addition but don't have to have. It is very difficult, technically, to explain to a patient, while he is going through these agonies of doubt, that in biting his nails he is having pleasure. Nor is it a great help to tell him, "Consciously you obviously have no pleasure, but unconsciously, while you are suffering, you are having pleasure." I advise you strongly not to make such an interpretation. Some patients have already read Freud and they will inform you that Freud said there is no unconscious pleasure, since an idea may be unconscious but not an emotion. Therefore it seems to be wiser to point out to the patient that what does take place is a discharge of what is the lesser evil. To the patient who bites his nails and suffers because of this, and therefore cannot understand that the biting should represent a satisfaction, I should say simply, "Stop biting for five or ten minutes. You will feel the tension and then you will see that the biting, although unacceptable to your total personality, does provide a certain relief."

Now let us go back to the structure of the neuroses. A patient suffers from his doubts, but while he is suffering, a certain discharge takes place. What kind of discharge? Why in this form? Perhaps it would be better if I first discussed briefly the cause of the obsessional neurosis, in accordance with the three parts of the total personality.

Those who read my book (Eidelberg, 1960) and remember the plot will perhaps recall that the patient was right. The patient is always right when he has doubts. This patient was the director of a candy factory and his real boss was his brother-in-law (who had married his sister, as it usually happens) and he had to obey him. He really hated this brother-in-law and he had the desire to get him into trouble. One day, at another factory, they found some kind of dirt in the candy. The factory was closed and the owner went to jail. Subsequently, while my patient was working in the laboratory he broke a bottle. Who breaks a bottle? Sometimes it is an accident. I will not say that we are entitled, whenever something happens, to jump to a conclusion and to say, "Aha." That is one of the words which patients like to hear. When someone breaks a bottle and for months thereafter keeps cleaning every place in the laboratory, constantly washing himself, and still has suspicions that little pieces of glass could be in his fingers, obviously there is reason to doubt that the breaking the bottle was purely accidental. It was caused by his desire to put little pieces of glass into the candy, to ruin the factory, and to get his brother-in-law thrown into jail. This interpretation, you are aware, cannot be revealed to the patient during the early weeks of treatment. It takes, as you know, an enormous amount of time before the importance and significance of the unconscious nature of the symptom can be explained to the patient. Some patients, like some of our critics, say, "Unconscious? Well, if they are unconscious we don't have to care." It takes a great amount of time, in fact it usually requires a full analysis, before you begin to understand the meaning of an unconscious wish. The unconscious wish in the case of an obsessional neurosis, in this case the wish to put glass in the candy, does not mean putting glass but, rather, some kind of dirt into the candy.

All obsessional neuroses, when analyzed, reveal the presence of anal wishes. In this case, the unconscious wish to put glass into the candy causes first the breaking of the bottle and second, the fear that the glass may really enter into the candy. What do I mean by saying this? Do I mean that the presence of a wish necessarily produces action? How often does a patient say to somebody else: "Drop dead." Nobody drops dead! In early childhood, there exists something which we call "omnipotence of thought" and an infantile wish is characterized by a number of factors. It is related to or connected with father and mother. It expresses a wish of one of the three stages of development and is characterized by the fact that in this stage the repressed wish still impresses the patient as if the wish and the action were the same. A little child may say, "I want to pee" when his pants are already wet. It takes time before he learns to separate the presence of the wish from the actual action. The neurotic does not differentiate between the wish and the action which gratifies the wish. In other words, when this obsessional patient felt like doing this act he reacted to the feeling of doing the act as if he had done it.

Every neurosis is the result of a defense. What you see is not simply the breakthrough of the infantile wish, but also of its defense. What is the defense? The defense in the case of a phobia is fear. The patient who refuses to cross the street, saying that there are too many cars, is right. There are too many cars in New York, but that doesn't produce his fear. The fear is due to the fact that he wants to be run over by the car and therefore he is worried. As long as he has this wish, there is danger that he will be run over. But this is only a superficial interpretation. The facts in a phobia are even more complicated. This patient even has the phobia when, while sitting in our waiting room, he has the fantasy of crossing the street. He experiences "fear" in our waiting room. What he really experiences is not fear, though he refers to it as such. He actually experiences terror. Fear usually increases our ability to deal with the problem. If I know that I will get some violent criticism I may become afraid of this criticism. I anticipate and I therefore speak better than I usually speak! But when I am in terror I collapse.

The patient who imagines that he is crossing the street, and unconsciously imagines that he is crossing it in order to be run over, reacts as if he were run over. He feels as if he has collapsed and therefore uses the defense of avoidance and stays home. In obsessional neurosis, the defense is different. This man theoretically could have developed a phobia. As a result of the phobia he would simply have avoided going to the factory. Often, in comparing certain illnesses, we are able to get a little deeper insight as to why it is that in one case a patient develops this symptom and, in another case, another one. Why the variation? We will not be able here to discuss the fascinating problem of what we call the "choice of neurosis." What I want to point out in discussing the structure of the obsessional neurosis is that the defense, in this case, is something which some of us call ambivalent oscillation, the doubting "Do I have glass, or don't I have glass on my fingers." This ambivalent oscillation is what many authors simply call ambivalence. It is slightly confusing, because in all three stages you will find ambivalence. Only after the phallic stage do you get rid of ambivalence. In an obsessional neurosis, there is something specific, a hesitation from one decision to another. This hesitation leads, descriptively speaking, to obsessive doubts. One moment the patient thought it was glass, then he did not and only with the help of his "slavemaster," in this case his sister, was he able, with this external help, to remove the obsession for a short time. We have said that the patient developed this problem because he had the desire to hurt, attack, destroy, and humiliate his brother-in-law, by putting glass or, since we are here in a scientific medium, by putting the feces into the food. As a defense against this kind of wish, he stopped the wish and he punished himself by developing this obsessional neurosis. He punished himself and he also punished, as so often happens, the whole family. His sister was forced to travel with him to keep the appointment with me, leaving her husband (the brother-in-law) alone in another city. She had to serve as his superego.

I assume you are fairly familiar with the division of the total personality into the id, ego and superego. You are also familiar with the fact that this is not a descriptive, but an explanatory concept. No analyst has seen the id, the ego or the superego. No analyst is supposed to see them. Should an analyst see a superego he wouldn't be an analyst and it would not be a superego. This is an explanatory concept that refers not to anatomical units but to certain functions. We can describe certain things better, so it seemed to Freud, when we realize that what takes place is the result of three basic dynamic centers: the id, which contains all the repressed wishes; the ego, which represents the executive power, and the superego, which is the moral or ethical representative, let us say the Supreme Court.

In the case at hand, the sister obviously represented the superego. In obsessional neuroses the patient very often uses somebody from the outside as his superego. His own superego is too sadistic. His own superego keeps on punishing him. His own superego tells him, "You wretch, you want to put glass into the candy." The only relief he can get is by projecting the superego onto the sister or somebody else who reassures him and, then, for a few minutes he can have peace. Hence, the symptom starts with the id, with the infantile wish, and is warded off by the ego serving partly under the pressure of the superego. The ego says, "No, you will not put the glass into the candy." This is done by using this special mechanism: "You will have to continually inspect your hands and because of that you will be unable to work and therefore there will be no danger that you could do any harm."

Analysis is able to help the patient only because what he is now suffering from is something which he needed, and very much wanted, long ago. It is what we call an historical misunderstanding. It is this anachronistic wish, which is the result of an unsuccessful repression, that remained in the patient and retained excessive infantile energy. Only when we have translated the unconscious wish into the conscious one, something which takes many, many months, is the patient able to find another method of dealing with the wish. One reason that we meet so much resistance, when dealing with the patient, is his fear that we are trying to take away a weapon with which he can deal with his wishes. He is afraid that, deprived of this weapon, he will simply give in and be overwhelmed by his infantile wish. In other words, the fear that the patient expressed in his resistance was that I, by taking away his doubt, would permit him to return to the factory and put the glass into the candy. Of course, an analyst is only interested in changing the existing method of defense into a better one. Instead of repressing and dealing with the problem on an unconscious level, using the expensive method of doubt, something cheaper can be used, namely, the rejection of this wish. "If I cannot get along with my brother-in-law, as I'm no longer a child, I don't have to stay home. I don't have to seek revenge in destroying him. I may go away, get another job and solve my problem in that way."

The infantile wish is characterized by the fact that the infant has so little power and so little choice. A grown-up person not only has more power but can move about, since he is not dependent on the family. The patient begins to realize that we are not on the side of the id, something which is difficult to conceive because so many critics of analysis continually claim that we are in favor of removing all the inhibitions of the patient. Where do the critics hear this? What analyst ever told them that he lets the patient beat him up? Or bring feces instead of money? It happens very rarely.

The idea that the analyst is on the side of the id, that he is in favor of giving up inhibitions, is obviously nonsense. I can only explain this by assuming that it is a projection of the critics' own infantile wishes. But perhaps we are also to be blamed. Some of us have the idea that psychoanalysis, being a science, is beyond what is good and what is evil, and that we are only scientists interested in finding out what is true and what is false and nothing else. A few months ago I heard from a student that a patient had asked him, "What will happen if

I don't come. Would you regret it?" The student thought that
he was supposed to say, "No, it would not make any difference." Whoever heard of such a story? Freud only warned
against exaggerated therapeutic ambition. But you cannot
analyze a patient unless you are interested in curing him. Even
if you are interested in analysis as a pure scientist, you can see
that something is true or not true only in terms of a therapeutic
change. As you are unable to hire people to be analyzed, you
can only analyze people who want to be helped. Therefore,
unless you are prepared not to tell the truth, you must have
a desire to help them.

Obviously, medicine is not pure science. Medicine is applied
science. That is also true of analysis, which is considered to be
part of medicine. The analyst is interested in finding the truth,
and he is certainly interested in curing the patient. As a matter
of fact, the only reason why we are entitled to look for the truth
and to be paid by the patient is because we are convinced that
finding the truth will help the patient. We are not simply fana-
tics of truth. Dealing with human beings we are entitled to
examine and to find out things only under the condition that
bringing into the conscious what was unconscious will have a
therapeutic effect. How can it have a therapeutic effect? Well,
if the unconscious wish which is still connected with childhood
becomes conscious the patient not only says, "Now that is conscious which was unconscious," but he also begins to realize
that he has partly lived in the past. In our illustrative case, the
patient recognized, in connection with a number of details,
that the brother-in-law and the analyst in the transference situation were not the analyst, nor the brother-in-law, but really
represented the father or mother. He recognized that he was
unable to differentiate between the wish and the action. If
he wished that I should drop dead, instead of having to feel
guilty, he would feel remorse. But remorse is something one
feels when one has done something wrong. The feeling of guilt
is a signal that one plans to do something wrong. The patient

may not be familiar with the difference in terminology, but when you explore the situation carefully, you see that when he says that he feels guilty, he actually feels remorse; he thinks he has done this thing and has to undo it, when actually he has done nothing. This recognition that he did not commit the crime he believed he had committed, no doubt gives him relief. However, it also brings him disappointment. In cases of depression, in cases of melancholic depression, the patient accuses himself of all kinds of crimes because he is unwilling to admit that what happened was not caused by him. When you succeed in proving the truth to him and getting him to realize that it is not his fault, he becomes furious, because part of his power, the power which exists in his fantasy, has been taken away from him.

To continue with the structure of the obsessional neurosis, we see a second characteristic of this defense mechanism: specifically, as a result of this defense mechanism, a symptom is produced. This is the compulsive symptom of thinking, "Do I have glass pieces or don't I have glass pieces." But is this always the case? Do we always have symptoms as a result of a fight between the wish and the ego and superego? No! We may also have a neurotic character trait. Schematically speaking, an obsessional neurotic with a symptom will, so to say, spend an hour thinking whether he should start with the left or the right shoe. He cannot make up his mind. By this, you realize that his complaint does not make sense and therefore you understand that his doubts are neurotic. The same problem, an anal wish and rejection of an anal wish, may, by ambivalent oscillation, produce not a symptom but a character trait. Instead of having the problem of deciding whether to start with the left or with the right shoe, another neurotic will spend four years meditating whether to go to law or to medical school. He will say, "Well, that is only a sign of my superiority. I'm not one of those who simply goes in to run and join. I want to examine the problem carefully." But what is he doing while slowly examining the problem? Most of the time he reads detective

stories or watches televsion. Technically, it is much more difficult to approach, understand, and, finally, to cure a neurotic
character trait than a neurotic symptom; the difference being
that although both are caused by the same kind of wish and by
the same kind of defense, in one case we have something which
is a foreign body and in the other case we have a neurotic character trait, something which we call ego syntonic. We really
should say syntonic with the total personality, but in the
literature you will find the term ego syntonic used. This ego
syntonic character trait, which appears very often on our
couch, has to be changed into a symptom to be analyzed. Before you start the interpretation, you have to prove to the
patient that what he considers to be a sign of his superior intelligence is actually something which is against him. Only
when he begins to realize that he wasted four years (not because he wanted to be careful before he made his choice), that
he had no choice, that he was forced to hesitate and waste time,
does he begin to see that this is the enemy within and only then
can the analytical interpretation be used.

We all know that each presentation requires a certain sim-
plification. There is no patient with a pure symptom neurosis.
I remember one patient who came to me with only one symptom: impotence. After a few weeks of analysis, I mentioned the
word "impotence" and he got very angry. I said, "What are you
talking about. That is why you are here." "Yes," he said, "but
one shouldn't mention such things. It is not very pleasant. And
then it is always possible that it is not really impotence. It may
be that the girl I had was not the right kind of a girl." You see,
he came with a pure symptom neurosis, but as a result of a few
weeks with me, he already was blaming the girl instead of ac-
cepting the responsibility. A patient who has a symptom, usually (unfortunately for beginners or students whom we would
like to provide with patients who have pure symptoms) also
has some neurotic character traits. These neurotic character
traits have to be changed into a symptom, a foreign body, be-

fore they can be analyzed. This change *cannot* take place by interpretation. This change can only occur by proving to the patient, with the help of his associations and other details, that what he considers to be an advantage is not one. For instance, you will find this in stinginess, in being a miser. In some ways the old saying "Penny wise and pound foolish" implies the same thing. The patient thinks that he is protecting himself against something. Actually, he is increasing the amount of difficulty. When Freud started with analysis, as you know, he avoided character neuroses. He was only able to deal with symptom neuroses. That is the reason why analysis now lasts so much longer and not because the patients are sicker or because we are less efficient. Our ambition is greater than before. We are not satisfied with dealing with the symptoms. We are trying, if possible, to deal also with the character trait.

So we have, in a superficial manner, described or compared the structure of a neurotic character trait with that of a neurotic symptom. Now if you go back to other symptoms and continue this comparison, you will find that there is a whole group of other symptoms which are characterized by complete lack of anxiety, different from a phobia, different from an obsessional neurosis, different from paranoia, and different from melancholia. We have something which is called a conversion symptom. It would be a mistake to assume that a conversion symptom is a sign of hysteria. While hysteria may sometimes produce conversion symptoms, it may also produce hysterical character traits and symptoms with anxiety, like phobia. The same is the case with the anal wishes. Under certain conditions, they produce an obsessional neurosis; in other conditions, the result is an obsessional character trait and, in another case, the result is a symptom. Most analysts are generally under the impression that stuttering is a conversion symptom caused by an unconscious, repressed anal wish.

DISCUSSION

Question: Does the patient, in feeling that he may get glass, which is a sharp object, in his fingers, imply an unconscious castration fear, or is he projecting a castration wish onto the brother-in-law?

Answer: Whenever we give an interpretation there is no doubt that there are many possibilities. The question is which of the many possibilities is the one which is present in this case. I have said what it meant in this case. How did I know it? Obviously, it is impossible in fifty minutes, or even in fifty hours, to present all the material which the patient brought to show that it had this and not another meaning. No doubt, in another case, glass may represent castration, but it may also represent the glass which was used to give him milk and may therefore relate to the oral stage. It may imply exhibitionistic and inspectionistic meanings. All the interpretations make sense only in connection with the specific associations which the patient has delivered. I would say, based on experience with many obessional neuroses, that while it is true that they have an Oedipus complex and therefore have castration fears, in the obsessional symptom it is not the castration fear which produces the symptom, but, rather, it is the anal wish. It would be obviously wrong to tell the patient, "You have an obsessional neurosis, therefore whatever you have represents feces." When you analyze obsessional neuroses, you find that one patient has doubts about having pieces of glass in his fingers, another thinks he has syphilis, and a third has still other ideas. Remember that the patient whom Freud (1924a) described in detail was afraid that when he didn't do certain things a terrible punishment would be inflicted upon his father: a rat would be placed on his anus and the rat would eat through it. In all these cases, the final material which you find connected with the symptom is the anal wish. But if you were to consider the whole material present in three or four years of analysis, obviously the Oedipus complex, the fear of castration, the wish to castrate father and to be castrated, all this would be present. Analysis is still an interesting profession because of the fact that what we are doing cannot be duplicated by a thinking machine. We cannot simply, by pushing a button, solve this and that. We have to select and find out, when we analyze the patient, what was actually the cause of his illness. The fact that the anal wish is responsible for obsessional symptoms was published long ago. It would have been much more interesting if I had discovered that in this case something else was responsible, but I did not.

Question: Would you give some more details on the process by which the character trait is formed?

Answer: This is the problem of the choice of neuroses. I am in agreement with those analysts who think that, in order to solve this problem, we have to be satisfied not only with finding the stage of development to which the symptoms belong, but we also have to try to determine to which libidinal type this patient belongs. In his short paper (1924) on libidinal types, Freud uses a quantitative approach. What do I mean by a quantitative approach, since we are unable to measure, in units, the amount of libido? In addition to measuring, there are other possibilities for making quantitative statements. One difference between America and Europe is this: in Europe they will say about a man "he is a tall man"; in America, they say, "he is a six footer." For Europeans, measuring is more complicated. Americans are more precise. Before Europeans are able to measure something in units, they are still permitted to say "this is bigger than that" or "this is smaller" or "this is equal." Freud suggested dividing all people, not only patients, into three basic types. One type in which most of the libido is present in the id, a second type in which most of the libido is present in the ego, and a third type in which most of the libido is in the superego. Now somebody will say, "Wait a moment. Just half an hour ago you said that nobody is able to see this libido. Now you claim to see whether there is more or less libido." Freud didn't claim that he was able to see the libido. What he said was this: some people make more of their decisions in order to gratify their id; there is another group where most of the decisions are made to gratify the ego; and there is still a third group which is chiefly impressed by the superego. Whenever we look around, we see that most people belong to mixed types, but here and there we find somebody whom Freud called an "obsessional type" (1924). It is not a very good word because it may be confused with obsessional neurosis. What he meant was that this type would be, descriptively speaking, very strict, very accurate, very conscientious. Whatever decision he makes, the most important thing for him is gratifying the superego. But there is another type who will be chiefly interested in gratifying the ego and a third interested in gratifying the id.

When a patient has an anal regression, it means that the patient, as a result of trauma, has a repression in the anal stage. If the anal wish becomes repressed, and if this patient belongs to the obsessional type in which the superego plays such a great role, he will develop an obsessional neurosis. If he belongs to the so-called narcissistic type, the type in which the ego plays the decisive role, he will develop a character neurosis. Why? The patient who makes most of his decisions from the point of view of the ego is unwilling to experience the presence of something which we call a foreign body. In order to avoid having a foreign body, he transforms this foreign body into a character trait.

Perhaps an example can illustrate this rather complicated theoretical material. There are people who, when they make slips of the tongue, blush and are embarrassed. Others are so afraid they will make a slip of the tongue that they don't talk. Then there is a third type, who, when he makes a slip of the tongue, says, "Well, isn't it charming?" So you see, you have three different reactions to slips of the tongue. Let us continue further with another illustration: blushing. There is one cause of blushing; it is usually an infantile, exhibitionistic wish. In one type, it produces a phobia of blushing. He stays home, "I may blush and therefore I stay home." In this type, the superego is dominant. The second type blushes, is slightly embarrassed, but finds it is not such a terrible thing. Then there is a third type, the narcissistic type, who blushes and says, "Imagine, a man of my age is still able to blush."

Freud (1933), in the second instinct theory, no longer divided instinct into sexual and ego instincts but into sexual and aggressive instincts. He assumed that we all have aggressive and sexual urges. But it is probable that the proportion or the quantitative relation between the two is not equal. Some people have more sexual wishes, others have more aggressive wishes. Perhaps the so-called libidinal type, the type where the id plays such a role, is the type where sexual wishes play, quantitatively, the greater role. In the obsessional type, the type where the superego is stronger, aggression plays the dominant role. We have seen again and again that the patient is always right. If someone has a strict ego, believe me, it is a good thing that he has such a strong ego, because he has so much aggression. Therefore, the same thing which may be harmless to the libidinal type is not harmless to an obsessional type, because of the amount of aggression he has. Therefore, the difference between a character trait and a symptom will depend on whether the greater quantity of the libido is concentrated in the ego or the superego. In analyzing such patients, in comparing different kinds of patients, you see that in obsessional neuroses, most of the time, you will deal with the superego. It is also interesting that it was in obsessional neuroses that the superego was first discovered. It was because there, even descriptively speaking, it dominates the picture. In a conversion neurosis, it is the id that dominates the picture. In analyzing, you are permitted to ask yourself not only what kind of wish, what kind of defense, is involved, but also to what kind of libidinal type does this individual belong?

Question: What about the practical application of these theoretical conceptions; how does one make use of them in one's work, such as in setting goals?

Answer: In dealing with the problem of the patient, we must take into account not only what he says, but what it means to him. You must recognize, in the patient who has a strict superego, that this strict superego is not necessarily caused only by the presence of infantile wishes. If we proceed to cure such a patient, he will be free of the neurotic superego, but he will still have a stricter superego than another cured patient, who belongs to the libidinal type or to the narcissistic type. We will not change the basic type. You can only change the neurotic part. Therefore, in setting our goal, we should not try to change the severe, but not neurotic, superego of an obsessional type.

Question: Could you say something about the role of the patient's piety in the therapeutic process? Also, how do we deal with the process of undoing and preventing it from being applied in the therapy, rather than in the resolution of the conflict? The patient with an obsessional neurosis is in the process of modifying the superego, so to speak. How does one recognize that he isn't modifying the therapist?

Answer: Let's start with the problem of undoing. Obviously, the patient whose wishes are repressed cannot be satisfied with the feeling of guilt. He must be interested in undoing because he thinks he has done something. I recall a patient whom I described in *Take Off Your Mask* (1960), who had the idea that when he touched someone in the bus when coming to see me, this person would die. In order to protect the life of this person, he had to go home and wash his hands and in that way he saved his life. It took him about six hours to get to my place, because he had to go and return a number of times. All of this was terrible suffering. But what a power. Just by washing his hands he saved a life and by touching a person he killed him. So when you translate an unconscious wish into a conscious one, this infantile omnipotent state in which the wish and the action are the same disappears. When the wish and the action are no longer the same, then obviously there is nothing you have to undo.

When we analyze a patient we never analyze his symptom or his character trait. We analyze the patient. We cannot concentrate on one thing, for the simple reason that our clumsy technique permits us to get into the unconscious only by the method of free association. There are many papers which tell you that by hypnosis or by certain drugs you can get the material much quicker. As if Freud had not started with hypnosis. We know this. But at the time he had the idea that the most important thing was to translate the unconscious into the conscious. Later, he found that the most important thing is to translate it while the resistance of the patient is being overcome. It would be without value, perhaps even harmful to the patient, to find out about his unconscious too early, before he is ready. Fortunately, his resistance has to be dealt with and therefore, he is protected from those analysts who are in a hurry and would like to give an interpretation he is not ready to take. So when you analyze the patient, when his infantile wish becomes conscious, when his infantile omnipotence is overcome, when he accepts the narcissistic mortification of recognizing that wishing is not the same as acting, then the necessity for acting out will disappear.

Our second problem is perhaps inspired by the famous case of the female homosexual, who, during her analysis with Freud, suddenly started to dream about having sexual intercourse with men. Freud (1920) then expressed the idea, rather unusual for him (but he didn't have to be Freudian), that this was a convenience dream or a transference dream. In each transference, there is a great amount of truth. The patient does it at first with you, it is easier to do it with you because he sees you only four or five times a week. Of course, I don't think that the real analyst will be only interested in hearing what is going on in the unconscious and what the patient did in child-hood. Obviously, from time to time, we want to know what else is going on in the outer world, what is going on, for instance, with his girl; we want to know the facts of his life. I will say, technically speaking, that whenever the patient talks too much about what happened during the day, I will try to get him to go back to the dreams and when he keeps on talking only about his dreams, I want to know how much money he has made this day. So the question, "is this only in the transference or is it already in relation to a real object," will be solved by seeing how the patient performs in reality.

As regards the third question, what do you mean by "piety"?

Questioner: The ceremonial and the ritual, that the obsessional compulsive employs, is sort of a pious approach to his way of life.

Answer: It is true that it has been said that the ceremonial of obsessional neurotics reminds us of the ritual of certain religions, but it is not the same thing. After the previously discussed patient's treatment was terminated, he stopped looking at his fingers, and he stopped asking questions, and he wrote me a letter in which he said, "Now, doctor, everything is fine and I'm really very happy. There is only one thing that still remains. I still wash my hands before I work." Such a habit does not have to be regarded as pathological.

Question: What is the relative efficacy of psychoanalysis as compared to psychoanalytically oriented therapy in the treatment of character neuroses and obsessional neuroses?

Answer: Of course, if you want an exact answer you will be disappointed. Having been an analyst for so many years and having also done a certain amount of psychotherapy, in those cases where no analysis was possible, I doubt very much whether you can change a character trait by psychotherapy. To answer is also difficult because when you say psychotherapy and I say psychotherapy, we might be referring to two different things. What is psychotherapy? Psychoanalysis is psychotherapy, since psychotherapy encompasses all therapies. Unfortunately, colloquially, the opposite meaning is used. Somebody who is not an analyst calls himself a psychotherapist, although, methodologically speaking, psychoanalysis is one form of psychotherapy. Now, if somebody is not a psychoanalyst, but has learned a certain amount of psychoanalysis, he will probably use a certain amount of psychoanalytical knowledge in his psychotherapy. How much he will use will depend not only on how much he knows, but how much the patient is able to take. How often this patient can come is also a factor. It is not so easy to draw the line. The simple differentiation that when the patient is on the couch it is analysis and when he is in the chair it is psychotherapy is nonsense. Unfortunately, many patients who visit their analyst five times a week and lie on the couch just get rest instead of analysis.

Question: Have you seen, in instances where there is no question of a diagnosis of an obsessional neurosis, instances of a flight into health? We would like to bring out more about the dynamic factor.

Answer: A number of analysts have seen this. You will remember that Freud (1962) himself wrote: "Falling in love may cure a patient." He once said: "What cures a patient is actually love, not the genital love, but the love of the analyst, the therapeutic love." Certainly, there are many patients who are getting better as a result of all kinds of factors. I think what is still so confusing, what makes the evaluation of what we do so difficult, is not only our failures, but also our success where there should be no success. So there are many factors which I don't know. There is no point in trying to pretend that we can be more exact. Now about the dynamic factor! When you raised that question, you wanted more information about dealing with the resistance. In psychotherapy, it is very difficult to concentrate on dealing with the resistance, because the patient is not seen often enough and is also not as secure as in psychoanalysis. I would say that the basic difference between psychoanalysis and psychotherapy, independent of the couch or the chair, is whether the resistance has been dealt with or whether the resistance has been avoided. Very often the resistance is not dealt with because the analyst is afraid of dealing with it.

Question: This raises another question, the other side of the coin. How often have we seen or do we see a flight into health, in cases of obsessional character neuroses?

Answer: This term, "flight into health" (Train, 1950), which was introduced some fifteen or twenty years ago, as opposed to flight into neurosis, no doubt represents something which can be observed. I would say that every patient tries to escape into health. Those whom we see are the patients who failed. There are many repressions in early childhood, but we are only familiar with what Freud called the unsuccessful repression. A successful repression does not produce symptoms or neurotic phenomena and therefore is not subjected to analysis. Psychotherapy, meeting somebody, changing a job, or maybe other factors, can all produce flight or fright into health. We don't know which factor is responsible.

In analysis, even in a long analysis, I do not know exactly what happens. I have a certain idea of what happens, what takes place, but there are always a number of things which remain unclear; so we cannot always say with great certainty exactly why they took place now or why they didn't take place before. For example, I remember a patient with oral problems, whose wish to devour the breast of the mother had been discussed for months. One day I used (I don't know why) the word "cannibalistic," and the patient said, "Why didn't you say it before?" "What do you mean I didn't say it before? I said, 'devour the breast,' that is also English." Well, for some reason, the word "cannibalistic" had not occurred to me, but even if I had used it before, it might have had no effect whatsoever. The patient was not then ready for it. Sometimes, a certain use of a word is helpful. Technically speaking, one should not make the interpretation dogmatic. I should have said "maybe you could find a better word." When, finally, one can arrive at some kind of verbalization which appeals to the patient, he suddenly has an emotional experience. The patient will say, "the bell rings," or "you hit the target," which means that the resistance has been broken through and he has finally experienced the presence of an infantile tendency.

Question: In dealing with these remissions or flights into health, there are many factors that have a great deal to do with therapy. If we are to assume that certain conditions require, for remission, depth psychology, then it means we must expunge the infantile neuroses. On the other hand, if we are just going to be filling stations and supply narcissistic gratification to overcome narcissistic mortification, then not as much talent or understanding of what goes on is required of what goes on in the interpersonal relationship, the transference, or disease mechanism. Many students are concerned with the question of whether depth therapy is essential in their treatment of neuroses. Obsessional character neuroses require depth therapy, otherwise the patient will never get well. He will have a short period of remission and is bound to run into trouble again. Do you feel you can comment on this matter?

Answer: Well, I would say, as far as I know from various discussions and from publications, that most analysts are under the impression that while the symptom may disappear or change to another symptom, a character trait requires analysis or a deep penetration in dealing with the resistance. If you do this, then there is little danger that the narcissistic gratification will help to overcome the narcissistic mortification, because the latter is so much more unpleasant and so out of proportion. The patient actually goes through steps or stages of suffering. It probably would be wiser if we could first cure the patient, show him all the things that a normal person can do and then start analyzing. That is technically very difficult. So we have to analyze first, go through all his agonies, to expect him to give up certain infantile mechanisms. We, too, provide, if not pleasure, at least gratification, because we promise him that one day he will cross into the promised land and then everything will be fine.

Question: You stated that you would not take up the question of choice of neuroses. Could you perhaps narrow down such discussion to the factors which influence the obsessional to make his choice?

Answer: I've already said that if you use the concept of the libidinal type and combine this concept with regression to one of the three stages, you have settled the problem of the choice of the neuroses (Eidelberg, 1954). If regression took place in the phallic stage, the result is hysterical neurosis: conversion hysteria if it is an erotic type; hysterical character if it is a narcissistic type; and a phobia if it is an obsessional type. There are neuroses as the result of oral wishes, anal wishes, and phallic wishes. In the phallic, we can have a conversion character, hysterical character, and the hysterias or phobias. Why one and not the other? It is because there is the libidinal type, the narcissistic type, and the obsessional type. If the patient belongs to the libidinal type and regresses to the phallic stage, he has a conversion hysteria. He stutters if he is at the anal stage. One must not confuse the localization of the symptom with the stage of regression. For instance, when a patient has hysterical vomiting, it is localized in the mouth but it doesn't relate to an oral wish, it relates to a phallic wish. The wish is usually "I want the penis of father." The beginner very often confuses the two things. The localization and the regression to one of the stages is not the same. In hysteria, if there is paralysis of the arm, it is not a regression stage of the arm, it is only the regression to the phallic stage, with the symptom localized in the arm. Why this is localized in the arm is not an accident. So, to continue, if the patient belongs to a narcissistic type and regresses to the anal stage, he is obsessional. If he is the obsessional type and is oral, he has melancholia. Regression to the anal stage leads to obsessional neurosis and in the phallic stage, to phobia and anxiety hysteria. This approach to the problem of the choice can be illustrated by the following diagram:

TYPE OF LIBIDO

Stage	Erotic Type	Narcissistic Type	Obsessional Type
Oral	Pseudodebility	Overt Homosexuality	Melancholia
Anal	Pregenital Conversion Neurosis	Overt Masochism, Obsessional Character	Obsessional Neurosis, Paranoia
Phallic	Conversion Hysteria	Hysterical Character	Anxiety Hysteria

Question: Could you discuss in a little more detail what you mean when you say that the patient is ready to understand his symptoms and his unconscious?

Answer: I would not, as I said, worry too much about it, because when you give an interpretation before the patient is ready, the patient will simply not take the interpretation. But as Freud pointed out, if that is your only contribution to his treatment then he will leave. Whether the patient is ready or not, depends on the material he brings. We usually try to hint at a certain thing. There are various techniques of hinting which you can use, but I cannot enumerate them at this point. To establish contact may be more important than to offer an interpretation. An analyst was once called in consultation to see a psychotic patient in a sanitarium. He entered the room and the patient, seeing him, took a glass from the table and threw it through the window. The analyst took another glass from the table and also threw it through the window. The contact was established. I don't mean that you should throw glasses through the window, but the problem is to establish a contact. Once you establish contact, you keep the contact and then you will see when the patient is ready, how he reacts, what you may dare to do, etc.

BIBLIOGRAPHY

Eidelberg, L. (1954), *An Outline of a Comparative Pathology of the Neuroses.* New York: International Universities Press.
—— (1960), *Take Off Your Mask*, 16. New York: Pyramid Books.
Freud, S. (1910), *Three Contributions to the Theory of Sex.* New York: Nervous and Mental Disease Publishing Co.
—— (1920), The Psychogenesis of a Case of Female Homosexuality. *Gesammelte Werke,* XII:271-302. London: Imago.
—— (1924), Uber die libidinösen Typen. *Gesammelte Schriften, 12:* 115. Vienna: Internationaler Psychoanalytischer Verlag.
—— (1924a), *Gesammelte Schriften,* 8:269. Vienna. Internationaler Psychoanalytischer Verlag.
—— (1933), *New Introductory Lectures on Psychoanalysis.* New York: W. W. Norton.
—— (1962), *Minutes of the Vienna Psychoanalytic Society-Volume I: 1906-1908, Minutes 1-53,* ed. H. Nunberg and E. Federn. New York: International Universities Press.
Train, G. J. (1950), Flight Into Health. *International Record of Medicine, 171:*2.

Family Diagnosis and Treatment: Some General Principles

NATHAN W. ACKERMAN, M.D.

The family approach to mental illness, family diagnosis, treatment, and prevention, has recently come into the public view. It stirs interest and controversy. In some professional circles it is popular, in others it is resisted; in the latter group it may be felt to be a threat to the established customs of thinking and doing in the sphere of mental health work.

Concerning family diagnosis and therapy, there are many questions. What is it? Is it an old or new idea? What is its rationale? Is it sound, appropriate, effective? What are its clinical indications, contraindications? What is its relation to individual psychotherapy and to the more conventional types of group psychotherapy? Should it be used alone, or parallel with other therapeutic techniques?

I shall try, briefly, to answer these questions. In mental health services to whole families, it is self-evident that the responsibilities of diagnosis and therapy run parallel. It is axiomatic that one cannot effectively treat a disorder without precisely assessing what is wrong. But, on the other hand, a therapeutically oriented interview is, itself, the royal road to diagnosis. By means of a clinician's engagement in the therapeutic process, he is enabled, stage by stage, to move toward an accurate and comprehensive diagnosis. Therefore, the procedures of diagnosis and treatment are interwoven and interdependent. On diagnosis rests the clarity and appropriateness of the choice of therapeutic goals, techniques, influence, etc., and it is the therapeutically oriented clinical interview that gives us the diagnosis.

It is to be borne in mind that despite the intimate connections of diagnostic and therapeutic procedures, they are essentially different. The diagnostic process, by its very nature, is total, while the psychotherapeutic technique is never so. It is always a partial, specialized kind of intervention on selected components of the disturbance. Up to the present time, we have had no single method of treatment of psychiatric disorders that could validly be called total. Each of the methods of which we have any familiarity achieves optimal access to certain levels of the disturbance. The potentials of influence, of each of these methods, arise out of the social structuring of the interpersonal situation and the specialized techniques employed. This being the case, it is understandable that, in facing the complexities of some psychiatric problems, we should employ multiple avenues of therapeutic entry and influence.

Family diagnosis and treatment signifies a special kind of intervention on emotional disorders. The unit of diagnostic evaluation and the unit of treatment influence is the whole family. The clinical interview is conducted with the functional family entity, the "primary patient" together with his family, because the unit of experience that is relevant to health is "the individual joined to his significant personal environment." It is within the network of family relationships that health is made or broken; therefore, the family as an integrated social unit is judged to be a useful point of entry.

The treatment of emotional problems in a family way is a "natural," an experiment true to nature. Families take to it "like a duck to water." By the family group is meant all those persons who have a functional participating role in the events of day-by-day family living. In the western community this is usually mother, father, and children, but may, in addition, include a grandparent, an aunt, and even the family maid.

The special focus of family psychotherapy is on the dynamic relations between the emotional functioning of the family as a whole and the psychological symptoms of any one individual member. Such treatment points its specific influencing power to the connections between interpersonal conflict in the family group and intrapersonal conflict in one person; in other words, to the balance of force between the conflict inside the mind and the conflict between that mind and the minds of other family members.

When the presenting complaint concerns the deviant behavior of an individual member, the family clinician simply and straightforwardly asks the whole family to come in and "talk it over." Contrary to the expectations of some physicians, the involvement of the rest of the family is not usually resisted. The conspicuous exception occurs when the clinician displays in his attitude something defensive, and apologetic, and self-consciously undertakes to justify the procedure. As soon as the clinician behaves in this manner, he conveys the idea that he may be doing something inappropriate or wrong. This method, the treatment of the whole family is not wrong; it is right. When the clinician invites the participation of the whole family in an easy, confident way, the members of the family are not only willing, but are even strongly desirous of the opportunity of coming in as a group to talk it over.

Is the idea of family diagnosis and therapy new or old? This it seems to me is, in a sense, a false issue. Let us simply say that, in the contemporary version, the procedures of family diagnosis and treatment are new. The more important question is not this, but rather, is the method appropriate and effective? So far as can be discerned, once the method is learned and carried out with confidence, there is no question about its appropriateness and its good results.

There has been confusion as to the definition of family therapy. Let us be clear, however, that we are referring to a true psychotherapy with the whole family. The claim is often incorrectly made, for other types of psychotherapy, that they are family treatment. This can be confusing. Individual therapy of one or another member of the family, or therapy of just the mother and child or just the husband and wife, is not yet a true family psychotherapy. These forms of intervention, it is true, exert certain partial effects on family relationships, but these effects are relatively nonspecific; they are indirect; they may either help or harm family relationships. As therapy, they focus on part processes, not the total functioning of the family as an integrated social unit.

The term true family psychotherapy means a specific method that intervenes therapeutically on the family as an "organism," based on systematic diagnosis of the family, a specific focusing on distortions of interactional patterns and a coping with the interplay between interpersonal and intrapsychic conflict. The basic orientation is to the ongoing relations of the individual and family group, as these pertain to mental health.

The rationale for family psychotherapy can be summed up as follows: it is a natural level of entry into human problems; it approaches troubled persons in their natural habitat, the home; and it defines human conflicts and disablements not in isolation, but rather in the matrix of significant relationships, the day-by-day intimate interchange among family members.

The inner emotional life of the family can make or break mental health among its various members. The ongoing emotional relations of the individual with his family exert a profound influence on the tendency of any one member toward health or sickness. These relations may affect the precipitation, the course, and the final outcome of the illness. The family emotional climate may fixate a member in his illness and reward him for staying ill; at the opposite pole, the family climate can influence the incentive for recovery. It is in this context that the processes of family interaction constitute an important factor in conditioning the processes of secondary emotional gain of illness. Similarly, family relations play a crucial role in determining a person's receptivity to therapy or his resistance to it, and, therefore, qualify the probabilities of recovery or the risks of relapse.

The validity of these principles rests on a simple truth: breakdown in mental illness is the product of deviations in emotional experience. Emotion itself is a social process. It is shared, reciprocated, and contagious. Since mental illness derives from deviant emotion, it is a contagious and communicable disease. The seeds of such sickness pass from person to person, from one generation to the next. They exist within the mind of the one individual and also move between the multiple minds of the family members. Over the stretch of time, the core of sick conflict shifts from one part of the family to another, from one individual to another, or one relationship to another. At a given point in time, the pathogenic forces which have contributed to breakdown can be traced in the here and now events in family living, even though, at the moment, these pathogenic processes may be differently organized and expressed. It is in this context that the chain of family relations represents a kind of conveyer belt, a carrier of foci of disturbance. It is well to bear in mind, however, that the chain of family relations also serves to transmit specific ways of coping with disturbance. The interplay between the shared patterns of control of emotion and individual defense against anxiety shapes the ways of struggling back to health. A further consideration, deserving of emphasis, is the principle that the network of family processes conditions the adaptation of the individual, not only to his several important family roles, but also to role relationships in the wider community.

The symptoms of disturbance in one family member reflect not only the psychopathology of his individual makeup, but are also a functional expression of the disorder of the family as family. In other words, one sick individual is the symptom of the warped emotional health of the whole family group. Moving a step further, in disturbed families it is almost never the case that only one member is troubled or emotionally sick. Generally, multiple members are disturbed and their disturbances interact in a special way that preconditions the ultimate outcome of their illnesses. Family psychotherapy, therefore, provides the opportunity for intervening on a cluster of interrelated illnesses, as contrasted with the limited therapy of a single patient. This logically leads to the whole challenge of prevention in the field of mental health, which is a chapter in itself. Suffice it to say here that the family approach offers potential powers of prevention of mental disorder that are in no way available through other forms of psychotherapy.

Let us consider method. The clinician's objective, in the therapeutically focused family interview, is to stir emotional interaction among the family members, and between them and himself. His aim is to activate an emotional interchange that is meaningful, while at the same time guiding the coping efforts of the family group to the specific core of pathogenic conflicts, both interpersonal and intrapsychic. The clinician endeavors to build a quality of rapport, of emotional communication, that may be referred to, figuratively, as a kind of "touching experience." In a deep emotional sense, he wants to feel touched by the members of the family and they in turn must feel touched by him. As a result, the members of the family come into better touch with one another. Of course, this is more easily said than done.

In family life, today, the breakdown of emotional communication is a serious problem. There is either too little of it because of the critical barriers that have emerged among family members, or if they do communicate with one another, they may do so too much, in the wrong way and about the wrong things. At one pole, there is the type of family that hardly communicates at all; the members of this group are fragmented and alienated from one another. At the other pole, there is the type of family in which the members are in contact, but they batter one another continuously and in a vicious way. In both instances, the mistrust and hostility is fierce. These people deny or displace the crucial troubles and conflicts. They may engage uncritically in a harmful scapegoating of one or another member; they may argue about the wrong issues. Loss of control is a constant threat and now and then actual violence breaks out. Some families oscillate between the extreme phases of killing silence and outbrusts of severe and violent fighting.

The aim of the clinician is to control and beneficially alter these abnormal processes of contact and communication. As far as he can, he endeavors to bring about an appropriate, vital kind of emotional interchange; a touching experience; a shared struggle to reach the crucial areas of unconscious conflict. He strives to avoid periods of hostile, unproductive silence, and at the other extreme, that utter waste of family contact and defensive argumentation about the wrong things or about sheer trivia.

In the therapeutic transference reaction between psychiatrist and family members, the clinician fulfills multiple roles—at times the part of the parent, on other occasions the grandparent or a sibling. He is interested and he is actively involved. He uses his therapeutic self in a special way. He activates an increasingly accurate and useful definition of the salient pathogenic conflicts. He confronts the family with them. He elaborates the recurrent expressions, and destructive consequences of these conflicts, not merely for one member, but for all. He articulates the ineffectiveness and harmfulness of the family's habitual ways of coping with these problems, their sick kinds of control and defense. He stirs an awakening of other avenues of possible solution or possible compensation of conflict. He encourages the discovery and substitution of healthy defenses in place of the pathogenic ones. Wherever needed, he injects more appropriate, more fitting emotions. He supplies the family with elements of emotional health which it had been lacking.

In the role of family therapist, therefore, the clinician is active, open, and forthright. In such treatment, it is not possible to be a passive listener or to hide one's face. In this therapeutic role, there can be no anonymity. The family therapist pitches in with the family, implementing, from his own being, the psychic elements which are missing in the processes of family interaction, the appropriate and needed emotions, and the more correct images of interpersonal relations and interpretations of motivation. He acts as a kind of catalyst or chemical reagent, dissolving the barriers to contact and communication, stirring interactional processes among the family members, shaking up the elements, and thus promoting an emotional matrix for a healthier realignment of family relationships.

The family members interact with the clinician partly in a real way and partly in an unreal way. Elements of transference are projected, along with elements of correct imagery of the actual qualities of the therapist's person. The therapist cannot be emotionally neutral. He must, from time to time, take the side of the weaker against the stronger or mitigate the destructive invasions of one member by another. He follows the movement of the center of pathogenic disturbance from one segment of the family to another. Frequently, a most intense focus of conflict emerges in the mother-child pair, and a child becomes scapegoated. The therapist may bring the conflict away from the child to the true area of conflict between mother and father. Wherever the center of greatest disturbance moves, it is the therapist's responsibility to follow along and engage in a process of working-through of the elements of conflict. As he does this he may also be required to offer selective support, now to this part of the family, now to another. Throughout the procedure, the therapist seeks to penetrate the pathogenic barriers to closeness and sharing in family relations. He cuts through levels of mistrust, despair, fear, and hatred. He challenges the existing patterns of alienation and fragmentation of family relationships. He questions the necessity for the splits and warring factions within the family group. He mobilizes action and reaction, and energizes release of hidden conflict material. He activates awareness of new avenues of sharing, new kinds of intimacy, and new levels of identification, and he stirs a realignment of family relations.

In so doing, he may call pointed attention to nonverbal expressions of the unconscious, such as facial expression, body postures, movements, etc.; by these means he may expand and sharpen the perception of relevant family conflicts. The discretionary use of these nonverbal level aspects of intercommunication is highly effective in this setting. It facilitates the therapist's ability to challenge unreal and impossible demands, fruitless, vindictive forms of blaming, and omnipotent destructive invasions of one member by another.

The characteristic conflicts and role disturbances within the family must be defined as to their intensity, their liability, and their location among the various members of the family. Within the patterns of contemporary conflict, one faces not only the components of pathogenic influence which have come up from the past, but also the potential resources of the family for solving or compensating conflict, so as to promote and maintain health. In this connection, it is of crucial importance to discern the dynamic relations between individual defense against anxiety and family group defense of the continuity of its essential functions.

The aims of the clinician, with respect to conflict, are: (1) to help the family to achieve a clearer and sharper definition of the real content of conflict—to spur a greater accuracy of perception and to resolve the confused interpretations of family conflict; (2) to counteract inappropriate displacements of conflict; (3) to neutralize the irrational prejudices and scapegoating which are involved in this displacement—the purpose here is to put the conflict back where it came from in the family role relations, that is, to re-attach it to its original source and attempt to work it out there, so as to counteract the trend toward prejudicial assault and disparagement of any one member; (4) to relieve an excessive load of conflict of one victimized part of the family, whether an individual or family pair; (5) to energize dormant interpersonal conflict, bringing it overtly into the life processes of family interaction, thus making it accessible to solution; (6) to lift unconscious intrapsychic conflict to the level of interpersonal relations where it may be coped with more effectively; and (7) to activate an improved level of complementation in family role relations.

Can it be done? The answer is unequivocally, yes. The complexities of family therapy are essentially no less and no more than the complexities of individual therapy. It is simply another method that needs to be learned; it takes practice and skill, but confidence comes with practice.

This method of family treatment may be usefully applied to a considerable range of psychiatric disorders in which the social determinants of breakdown and mental disorders loom large. In a general sense, intervention in a family way can be helpful with neuroses, character disorders, psychosomatic conditions, and some of the functional psychoses. For optimal progress, all members of the family unit need to be involved; one needs assurance that the emotional forces supporting union in the family are stronger than the forces pushing toward destruction and alienation. Of course, in the final analysis, progress depends upon the therapeutic skill and special training of the clinician.

Family therapy can be of material value for disturbances at all ages of the life cycle, childhood, adolescence, adulthood, and also old age. It is, surely, especially potent in disturbances involving the relations of a child to the family. Family psychotherapy can be the method of choice, it can be the sole method, or it can be used in conjunction with other procedures. It is helpful when one adult member of the family is entering individual psychotherapy; it is similarly helpful toward the termination of a period of individual therapy. It is especially valuable in dissolving patterns that reinforce the secondary neurotic gains which impede a given member's progress in therapy.

On the contemporary scene, the impact of revolutionary social change, the turbulence of human goals and values, the agitation of human relationships, and the fluid and unstable character of the present day family, all challenge us to a searching scrutiny of social processes; in particular, it invites the clinician to undertake a penetrating analysis of the relations of the family phenomenon to health.